D1228523

VOLUME 3
Oceans

MICHAEL ALLABY

About This Set

BIOMES OF THE WORLD is a nine-volume set that describes all the major landscapes (biomes) that are found across the Earth. Biomes are large areas of the world where living conditions for plants and animals are broadly similar, so that the vegetation in these locations appears much the same. Each of the books in this set describes one or more of the main biomes: Volume 1: The Polar Regions (tundra, ice cap, and permanent ice); Volume 2: Deserts (desert and semidesert); **Volume 3: Oceans** (oceans and islands); Volume 4: Wetlands (lakes, rivers, marshes, and estuaries); Volume 5: Mountains (mountain and highland); Volume 6: Temperate Forests (boreal coniferous forest or taiga, coastal coniferous forest, broad-leaf and mixed forest, Mediterranean forest and scrub); Volume 7: Tropical Forests (rain forest and monsoon forest); Volume 8: Temperate Grasslands (prairie, steppe, and pampas); Volume 9: Tropical Grasslands (savanna).

The books each have three sections. The first describes the geographical location of the biome, its climate, and other physical features that make it the way it is. The second section describes the plants and animals that inhabit the biome and the ways in which they react to each other. The final section of each book deals with the threats to the biome and what is being done to reduce these. An introduction in Volume 1 includes a map showing all the biomes described in this set, and a map showing all the countries of the world.

Throughout the pages of this set there are diagrams explaining the processes described in the text, artwork depictions of animals and plants, diagrams showing ecosystems, and tables. The many color photographs bring each biome to life. At the end of each book there is a glossary explaining the meaning of technical words used, a list of other sources of reference (books and websites), followed by an index to all the volumes in the set.

Published 1999 by Grolier Educational, Danbury, CT 06816

This edition published exclusively for the school and library market

Planned and produced by Andromeda Oxford Limited, 11–13 The Vineyard, Abingdon, Oxon OX14 3PX, UK

Project Manager: *Graham Bateman*
Editors: *Jo Newson, Penelope Isaac*
Art Editor and Designer: *Steve McCurdy*
Cartography: *Richard Watts, Tim Williams*
Editorial Assistant: *Marian Dreier*
Picture Manager: *Claire Turner*
Production: *Nicolette Colborne*

Origination by Expo Holdings Sdn Bhd, Malaysia
Printed in Hong Kong

Set ISBN 0-7172-9341-6
Volume 3 ISBN 0-7172-9344-0

Biomes of the world.
p. cm.
Includes indexes.
Contents: v. 1. Polar regions -- v. 2. Deserts -- v. 3. Oceans -- v. 4. Wetlands -- v. 5. Mountains -- v. 6. Temperate forests -- v. 7. Tropical forests -- v. 8. Temperate grassland -- v. 9. Tropical grassland.
Summary: In nine volumes, explores each of the earth's major ecological regions, defining important features, animals, and environmental issues.
ISBN 0-7172-9341-6 (hardcover : set : alk. paper). -- ISBN 0-7172-9344-0 (hardcover : vol. 3 : alk. paper)
1. Biotic communities--juvenile literature. 2. Life zones--Juvenile literature. 3. Ecology--Juvenile literature. [1. Biotic communities.] I. Grolier Educational (Firm)
QH541.14.B57 1999
577--dc21 98-37524
CIP
AC

Contents

The Physical World of Oceans

It is not until your ship has been at sea for about three hours that you really start to experience the ocean. When you have been out of sight of land for some time, when even the sea birds have gone—for most of them do not venture far from land—it seems water covers the entire world. Earth, you may think, is a planet with a surface mainly of water.

THE WORLD'S OCEANS AND THEIR CURRENTS. The oceans predominate in the Southern Hemisphere much more than in the Northern Hemisphere. In addition to the Atlantic, Pacific, Indian, and Arctic Oceans, there is the Southern (Antarctic) Ocean, which encircles the Antarctic continent. In each ocean there are currents carrying warm water (shown here in red) away from the equator and cool water (shown in blue) toward the equator. This transport has an important influence on the world's climates. Also shown are major coral reef areas, which have their own unique life.

This impression is not far from the truth. Look at a photograph taken by a satellite showing our planet as a bright sphere floating in the blackness of space, and the world appears blue, white, green, and brown (see page 7). Blue is the color of the oceans—large masses of salt water in enormous basins. White is the color of the clouds and of the snow and ice around the North and South Poles and high on mountains. Green and brown are the colors of the land.

There are five oceans: the Atlantic, Pacific, Indian, Arctic, and Southern (Antarctic), although three of these—the Atlantic, Pacific and Indian—are regarded as the principal oceans. The Arctic Ocean is regarded by some researchers as part of the Atlantic. The Southern Ocean is really the southernmost part of the Atlantic and Pacific. It is bordered by the continent of Antarctica to the south, but has no land bordering it to the north.

The Pacific, including the sections of the Southern Ocean, accounts for about 46 percent of the area of marine waters.

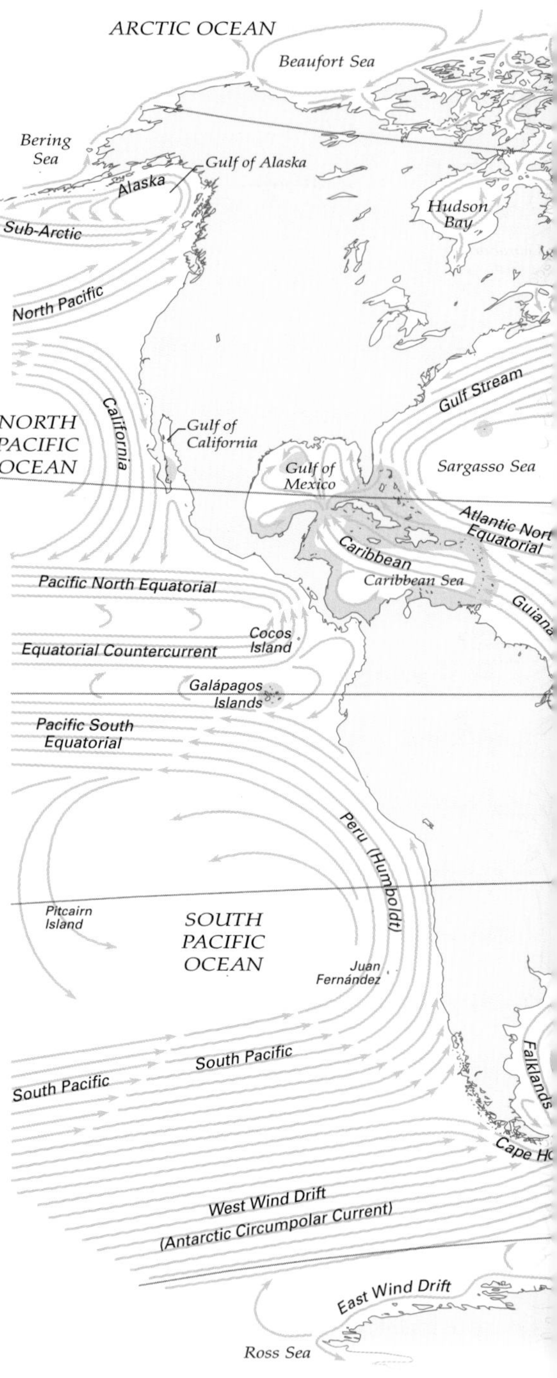

The oceans include seas—smaller expanses of marine waters. Among the largest seas are the Mediterranean, Caribbean, Yellow, South and East China Seas, and the Sea of Japan.

Oceans cover more than two-thirds of the Earth's surface (70.8 percent). That means salt

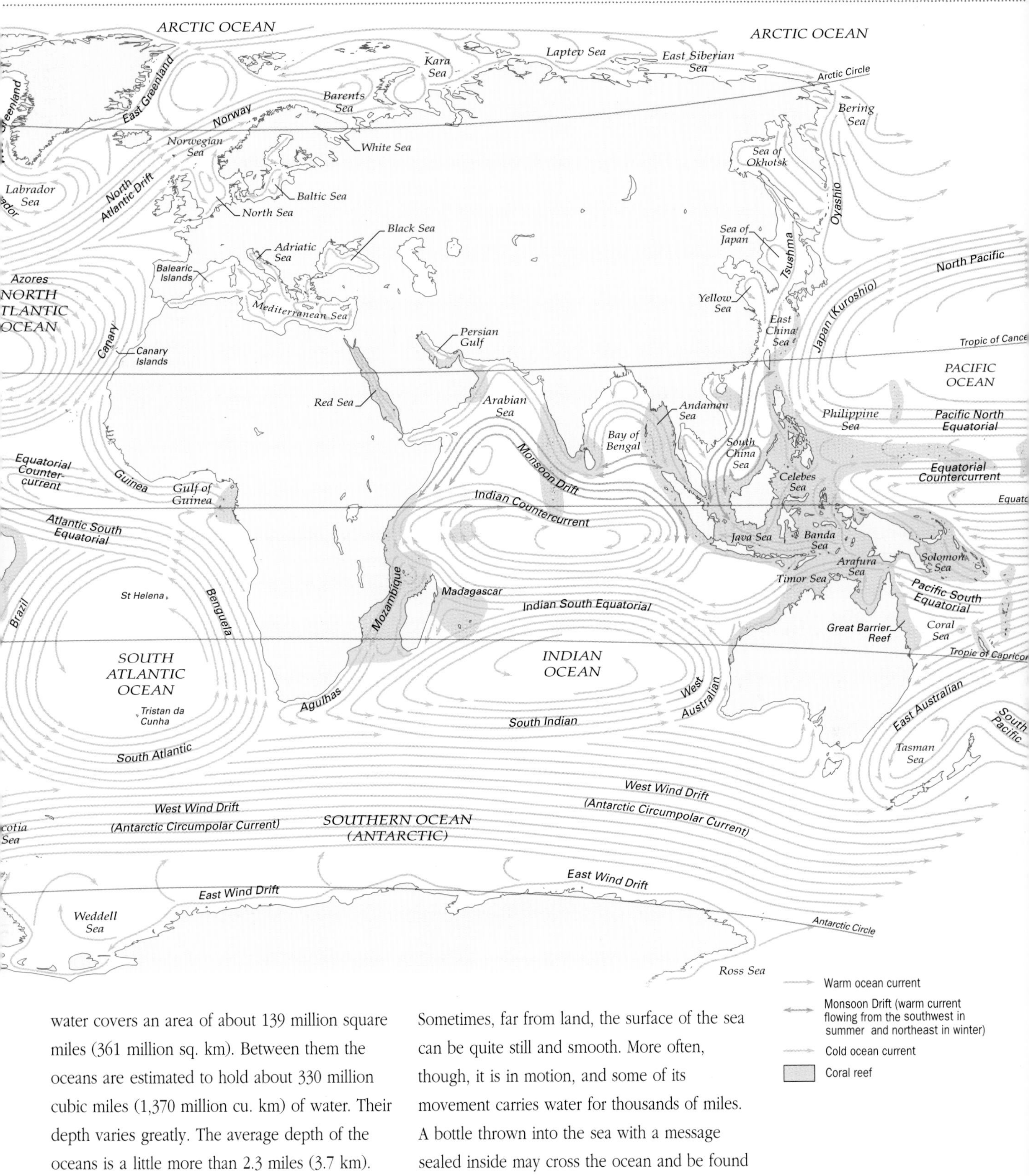

water covers an area of about 139 million square miles (361 million sq. km). Between them the oceans are estimated to hold about 330 million cubic miles (1,370 million cu. km) of water. Their depth varies greatly. The average depth of the oceans is a little more than 2.3 miles (3.7 km).

Sometimes, far from land, the surface of the sea can be quite still and smooth. More often, though, it is in motion, and some of its movement carries water for thousands of miles. A bottle thrown into the sea with a message sealed inside may cross the ocean and be found on the coast of another continent. The bottle floats with an ocean current (see page 11). There are major currents in every ocean. They strongly affect the world's climates, by carrying warm water away from the tropics and replacing it with cool water.

You might think size is the only difference between an ocean and a sea. Oceans are large, seas are much smaller and usually partially surrounded by land. There is also a more important difference. Seas and oceans both fill depressions, called basins, in the rocks that form the crust of the Earth, but the crust is not the same everywhere. Rock that forms the crust beneath the oceans differs from the rock forming the crust of the continents, and many seas form in depressions in continental crust. That is why seas are always close to land.

It is not only the surface of the ocean that moves. So does its floor. Look at a map of the world, and you will see that some of the continents look as though they once fit together. South America fits into Africa, for example. What is more, the rocks in West Africa are of the same type as those in South America, and the same kinds of plants and animals are found on lands separated by thousands of miles of sea. These continents were once joined and have broken apart.

WANDERING CONTINENTS

Scientists have managed to trace the paths taken by the continents over millions of years. At one time all the continents were joined together in a single supercontinent. This has been called Pangaea (the name is from the Greek, and means, literally, all-earth). A little more than 200 million years ago Pangaea began to split in two. Then there were two supercontinents. The northern one was Laurasia, the southern one Gondwanaland, or Gondwana. Each of them began to divide, producing the continents we see today, but they were not where they are today. Fifty million years ago, for example, the North Atlantic was much narrower than it is now.

The continents are still moving, carried by the rocks being pushed and pulled this way and that by changes taking place on the ocean floor. North America and Europe are drifting apart by about 3 inches (8 cm) a year. It is hard to imagine something that happens so slowly, except by parallels; if, for example, you never cut your toenails in the course of a year, they would grow by just about 3 inches.

For a long time scientists, too, were rather doubtful about the idea of moving continents and spreading seas. They

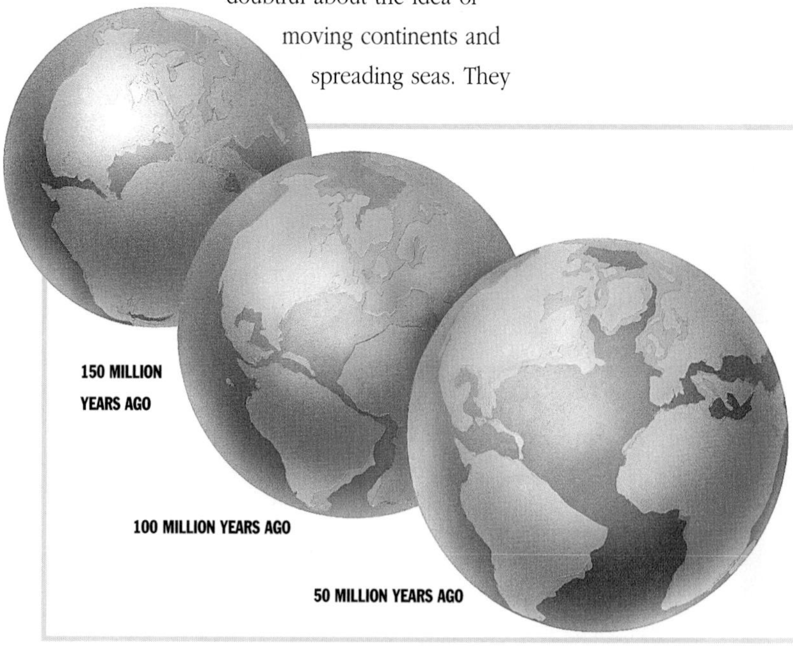

FROM SPACE it is easy to see that most of the Earth's surface is covered by water. In this satellite photograph the blue areas are ocean, and the white areas cloud (made from water droplets). The brown and green areas visible beneath the cloud are North, Central, and South America.

150 MILLION YEARS AGO

100 MILLION YEARS AGO

50 MILLION YEARS AGO

TODAY

THE EARTH OVER 150 MILLION YEARS. About 200 million years ago the supercontinent of Pangaea broke up; the continents then started to move. Oceans also change size. At present the Atlantic is widening, causing Europe and North America to move apart at a speed of about 3 inches (8 cm) a year.

could not see how something the size of a continent could wander over the face of the Earth. But gradually an explanation emerged. Continents drift, and sea floors grow larger or smaller because the Earth's crust consists of sections that move. This is called the theory of plate tectonics.

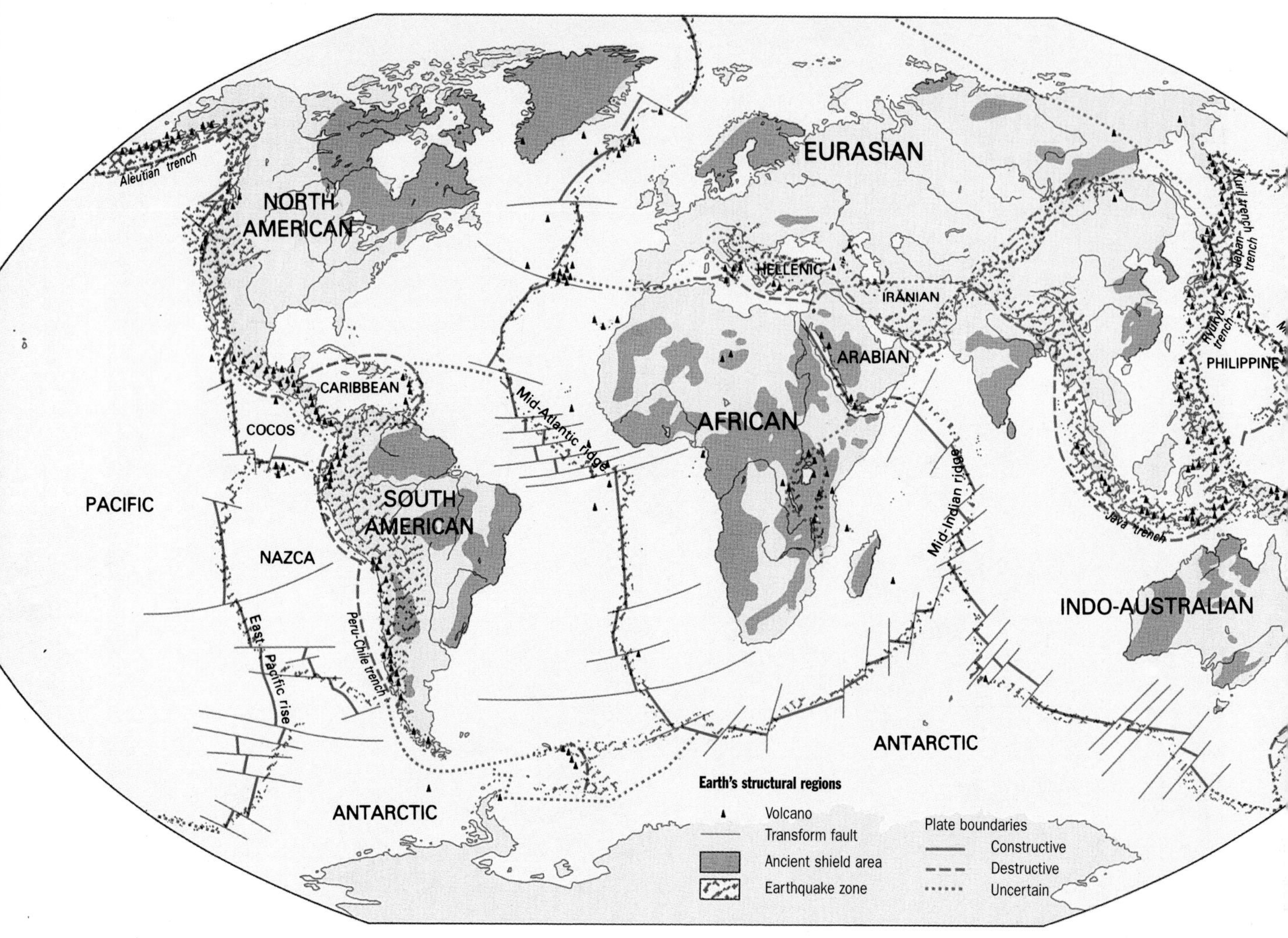

THE EARTH IN MOTION

Tectonic (in its geological sense) means resulting from distortion. The Earth's surface is distorted—folded, twisted, broken, or pushed somewhere new—by movements in the rocks near the surface of the Earth. These rocks provide the solid ground on which we stand and compose the Earth's crust, or surface layer.

Compared with the size of the whole planet, the crust is very thin. Beneath the oceans it is no more than about 3 miles (5 km) thick. It is thicker beneath the continents—which is why the continents stand high above the sea. The thickest part is found in mountain ranges. In the Himalayas, for example, the crust is up to 50 miles (80 km) thick.

The Asthenosphere and the Lithosphere

Beneath the solid, cold rocks of the crust there is rock so hot it is able to move. It forms a thin, semimolten layer of the Earth called the asthenosphere. The rigid outer layer of the Earth, including its crust, seals in the asthenosphere. It is called the lithosphere.

THE EARTH'S CRUST consists of plates of rock that can move. The boundaries, or margins between plates, are "constructive" if new material is being added, "destructive" if material is being lost, and "conservative" if material is being neither added nor removed. Where a plate is forced under another, a deep trench forms. Plates move past one another along "transform faults."

Plates on the Asthenosphere

The lithosphere is not a single, complete cover. It consists of rigid blocks, called plates, floating on the semimolten rock of the asthenosphere. Some are large, others small. Some are moving in relation to one another, others are still. Some ceased moving long ago, and the boundaries, or "joints," between them are firmly closed and locked. These joints are often found in the middle of continents.

Continents rise from the surfaces of the plates, but the plates extend far beyond the coastlines. The North American and Eurasian Plates meet in the middle of the North Atlantic. Australia and India are both on the same Indo-Australian Plate.

South America and Africa are on plates that meet in the middle of the South Atlantic. These continents are moving apart, like those on either side of the North Atlantic, because their plates are growing larger. New material is gradually being added along a line passing down the middle of the ocean.

Volcanoes are openings in the Earth's crust from which molten rock and dust from below the surface is ejected. They can form under the sea. Molten rock, called magma, rises from the asthenosphere in submarine volcanoes. Magma, known as lava when it erupts, cools quickly in the cold water of the deep ocean and then solidifies, forming a solid mass of rock on either side of each volcano.

Ridges and Margins

The submarine volcanoes produce a long mountain range. This is called a mid-ocean ridge, and it marks the line where two plates meet.

HOT LIQUIDS rushing through gaps in the Earth's crust look like smoke because of the chemicals dissolved in them. They are called smokers. Depending on their chemical composition, some are black smokers, and some white smokers. Large communities of bacteria, worms, crabs, and other animals live around smokers.

The boundary between two plates is called a margin. A margin with a ridge, where new material is being added, is a "constructive" margin. There are also "destructive" margins, where material is being lost and where the edge of a plate is sinking below that of another.

The continual addition of new rock at the center of the ridge pushes the plates apart. Set on their plates, the continents drift away from each other, and the ocean between them grows wider. The theory of this movement is called continental drift. As some oceans are growing wider at ridges, others are shrinking.

THE OCEANIC CRUST. At a mid-ocean ridge hot rock—magma—rises to the surface. It cools and solidifies as a rock called basalt and in time is buried beneath sediment sinking from above. Farther away rock called granite forms the continents. This is less dense than basalt, so it is bulkier, making the Earth's crust much thicker beneath continents than it is beneath the oceans.

Where two plates collide, one sinks below the other—the process is called subduction. The rock from which the plate is made returns below the crust. Sometimes sediments that have accumulated on the surface of the crustal rock are not subducted, but crumpled upward to form mountain ranges. The northward movement of the Indo-Australian Plate has caused it to collide with the Eurasian Plate, and that collision has produced the Himalayas. The movement has not ended, and the mountains are still rising.

Elsewhere plates are being neither formed nor destroyed. They move past each other in sudden, jerky lurches. These lurches can cause earthquakes. Not surprisingly, earthquakes and volcanic eruptions are most violent and happen most frequently in regions that are close to the plate margins.

ICE AGES AND OCEAN CURRENTS

All this drama on the sea bed is hidden from us beneath the water. You might think that oceans and seas always contain the same amount of water. But the amount sometimes changes, and when it does, the level of the sea rises or falls.

Changes in sea level are due mainly to variations in the size of the polar ice caps and glaciers. During ice ages (glacial periods) the ice covering Antarctica and Greenland grew thicker and expanded to cover a larger area of the Earth's surface.

The water to make that ice came from snow; that in turn was made from water evaporating from the oceans. Because there was markedly less water in the oceans, the sea level was lower.

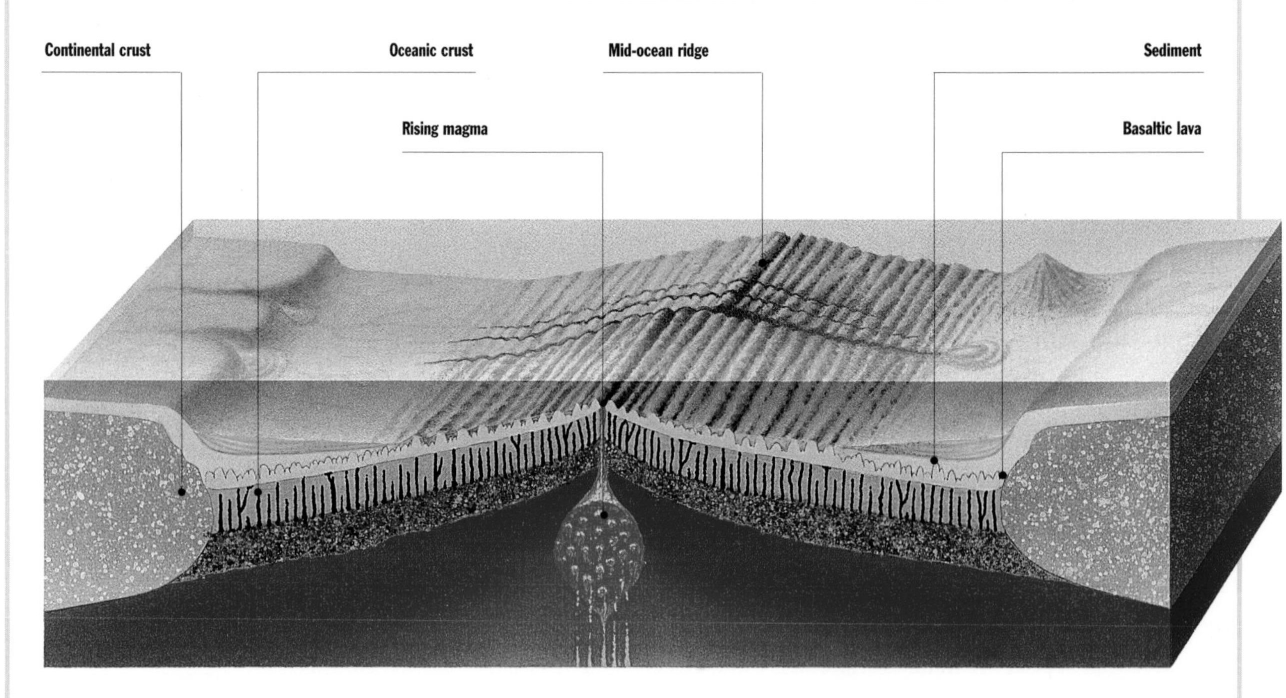

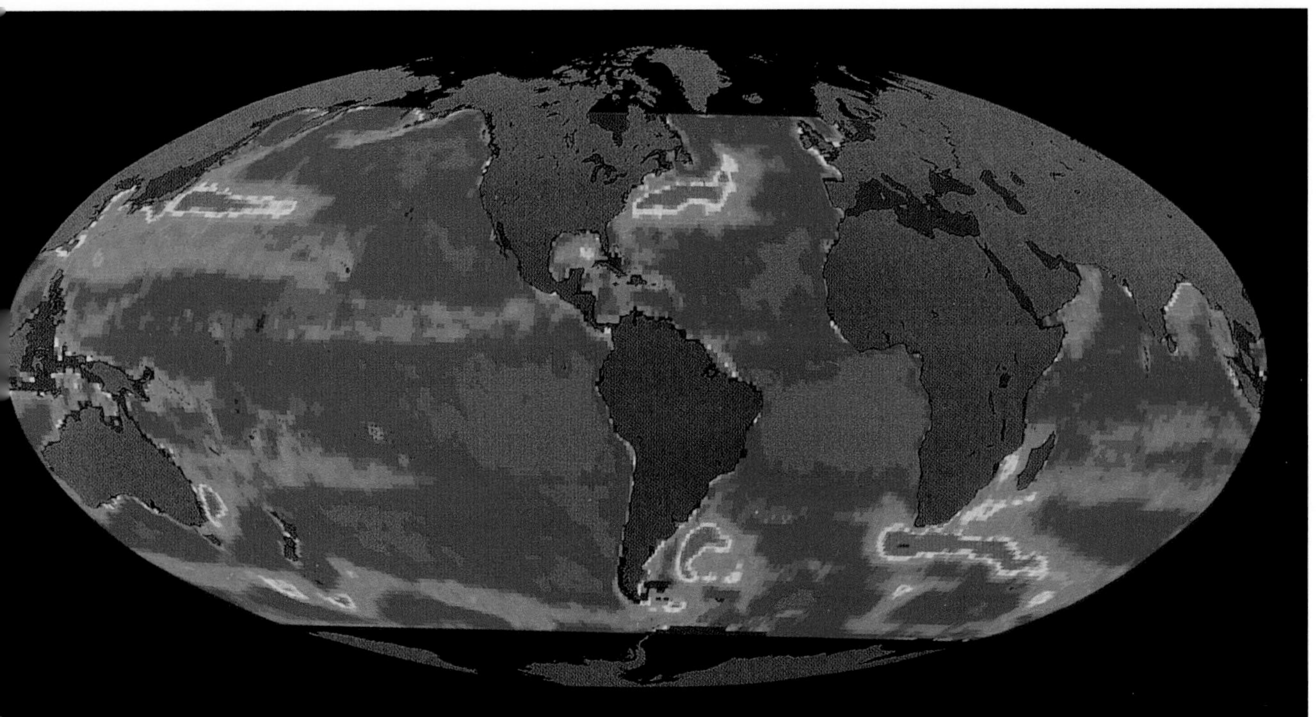

OCEAN CURRENTS. The warm ocean currents, shown here in red bordered with yellow, flow roughly in circles, called gyres. They flow on the western sides of oceans and are quite fast. Cold currents are slower, and some of them flow deep below the surface. The principal warm currents are the Kuroshio off Japan (top left in the picture), Gulf Stream off the North American coast (top center), Brazil off the South American coast (bottom center), and Agulhas off southern Africa (bottom right).

When the climate grew warmer, the ice melted, the water flowed back into the sea, and the sea level rose again.

Low tides occasionally expose the remains of what were once forests. (These are quite common off the west coast of Great Britain.) There are also places, high above the sea, where sand and seashells indicate there was once a beach. These illustrate times when the sea level has been lower or higher than it is today.

Warm Water and Cold

Near the poles, in the far north and south, the sea is always cold, and in winter its surface freezes. When water freezes, any substances dissolved in it are "squeezed out" from the ice. Try making ice cubes from salt water, and you will find the ice does not taste salty, but some very salty water is left at the bottom of the tray. The same thing happens when the sea freezes. At the edge of the ice the sea is saltier than it is farther away. Salt water is denser than fresh water because of the salt in it. Water also reaches its maximum density at 39°F (4°C), just above freezing.

At the edge of the sea ice the water is denser because it is very salty and also because it is almost freezing. This very dense water sinks. In the North Atlantic, near Greenland, it sinks all the way to the bottom of the ocean and then flows south, very slowly. It is called the North Atlantic Deep Water (NADW), and it travels all the way to Antarctica. There, the Antarctic Intermediate Water (AIW) forms. It is not especially salty, but as it flows north, it sinks to a depth of about 3,000 feet (900 m) beneath the warmer, less dense water.

Cold water flowing toward the equator is replaced by warmer water, and this exchange of water produces the principal ocean currents. They flow in approximate circles, called gyres, in all the oceans.

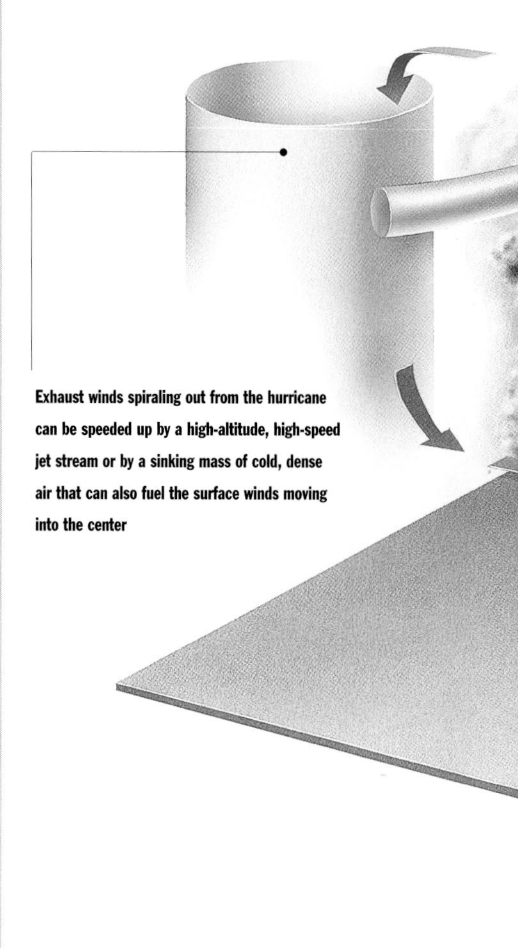

WINDS AND STORMS

Prevailing low-level winds drive the ocean currents, which move in large circles, called gyres. At high level the winds are different. There are two regions (at about 30° and 50°) in both the Northern and Southern Hemispheres where warm and cold air meet. The difference in temperature and density between the warm and cold air is most pronounced at about 40,000 feet (12 km). This causes narrow belts of very strong, high-altitude winds called the subtropical and polar jet streams. These blow from west to east in both hemispheres. Weather systems form beneath the jet streams. They can cause severe weather, including storms at sea.

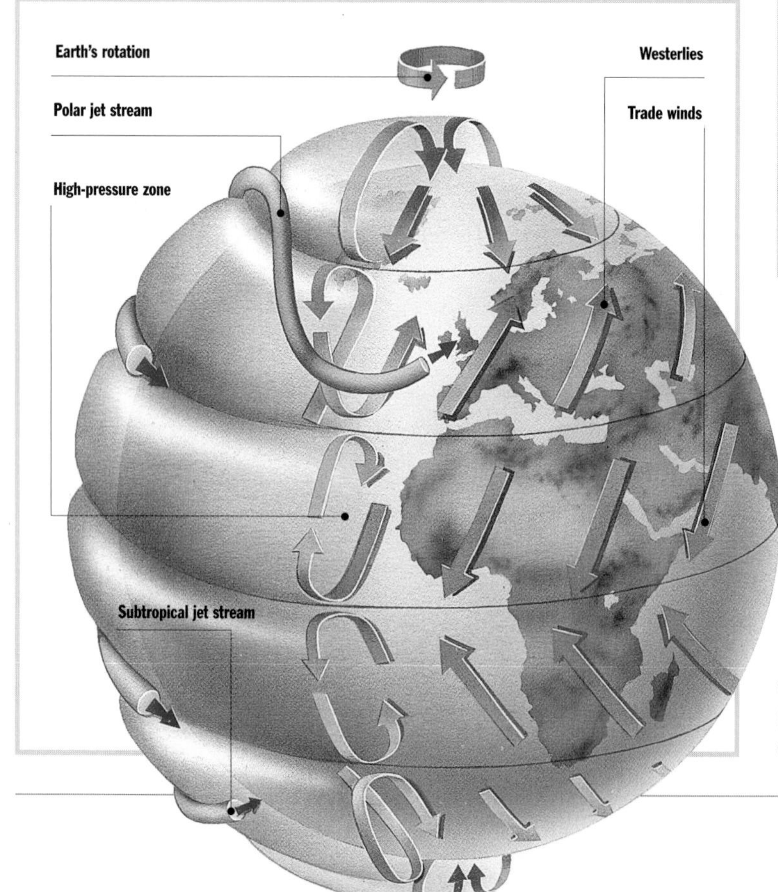

WINDS AND JET STREAMS. **Warm air rises over the equator, then flows away from it at a great height. It cools and sinks in the tropics to create high-pressure zones. From there most of it flows back toward the equator, forming the so-called trade winds, but some of it flows away from the equator. Cold air sinks over the poles and flows outward. Where it meets warm air from the tropics in the middle latitudes, the air rises. This produces a belt of westerly winds ("westerlies"). Where cold and warm air meet at high altitudes, they cause narrow belts of strong winds in both hemispheres. These are the polar and subtropical jet streams.**

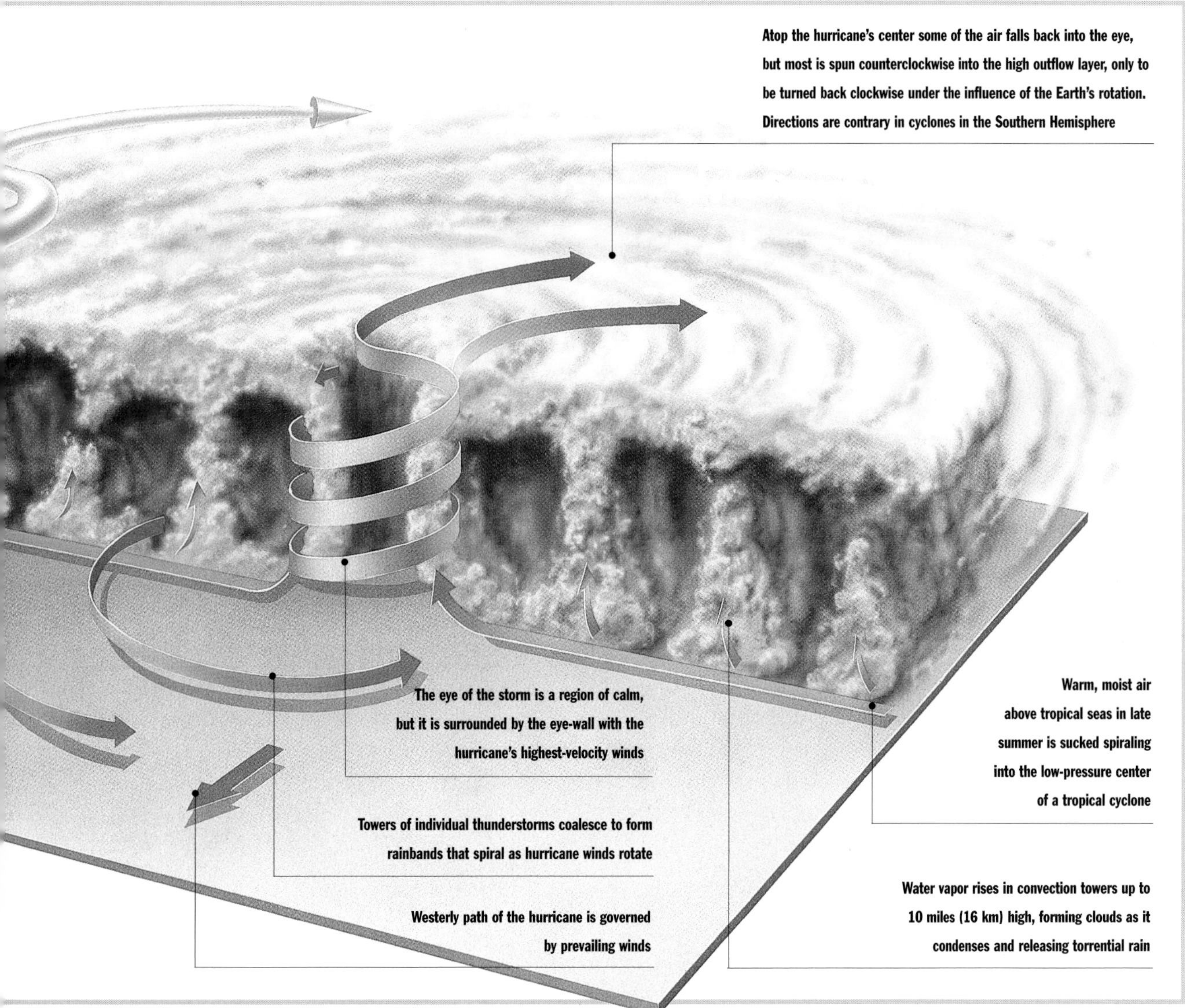

Hurricanes, Typhoons, and Cyclones

In the tropics the sea is sometimes very warm: its temperature can reach 80°F (27°C). By late summer, when it has had time to warm up, huge amounts of water evaporate from it. The water vapor rises and condenses to form towering clouds. These produce heavy rain and storms.

If rising air is being swept away by a strong wind at a height of about 50,000 feet (15,250 m), the storm may grow bigger. It starts revolving as a huge spiral up to 300 miles (480 km) across. Air pressure is very low around its center, where air is spiraling upward. Air flowing into the spiral accelerates, and the wind speed can be 150 mph (240 km/h).

Scientists call this type of storm a tropical cyclone. If it forms in the Atlantic, it is a hurricane, in the Pacific or China Sea it is a typhoon, in the Indian Ocean it is a cyclone. There are several more local names, including willy-willy (Australia) and baguio (Philippines). This is the most dangerous storm on Earth.

HURRICANE FORMATION. Violent tropical storms (also called hurricanes, typhoons, and cyclones) develop where the sea is relatively warm. They are the most violent and dangerous storms.

The Natural World of Oceans

Beneath the surface of the ocean there lies a hidden world inhabited by plants and animals we rarely see. Like species that live on land, they have adapted to the specific demands of their environment.

Sometimes the sea looks green. It is green because floating in it are countless millions of green plants—algae. Each consists of only one cell, but it contains chlorophyll, the green pigment that absorbs sunlight to provide the energy for photosynthesis—the production of organic compounds by plants.

On land green plants provide food for animals. It is just the same in the sea. There, small animals graze on the single-celled plants and, just as on land, the plant-eaters are hunted by bigger animals.

Even the animals living far below in the permanent darkness of the very deep ocean depend on the plants floating in the sunlight. When the plants and surface animals die, they sink down, falling like rain on the sea bed and providing food for another animal community.

All these plants and animals drift with the tides and currents. They are wanderers. The Greek word for wandering is *planktos*, and these tiny wandering organisms are called plankton. The plants among them are phytoplankton, and the animals are zooplankton. Apart from the single-celled plants and animals, the plankton includes small crustaceans, or arthropods with a hardened carapace—a group that includes prawns, shrimps, lobsters, woodlice and barnacles—and the larvae of bigger animals, including fish.

Plants need sunlight, water, and carbon dioxide for photosynthesis. These are plentiful for plants that float in the water. Plants also need a range of other elements, and these are not so easy to find in the ocean. The elements needed in relatively large amounts include nitrogen, phosphorus, potassium, calcium, and magnesium. Others are required in very small

KELPS *(opposite)*, one of the biggest of all seaweeds, often form extensive underwater forests. Their wavy-edged fronds, up to 90 feet (27 m) tall, sway gently in the currents, like trees in the wind.

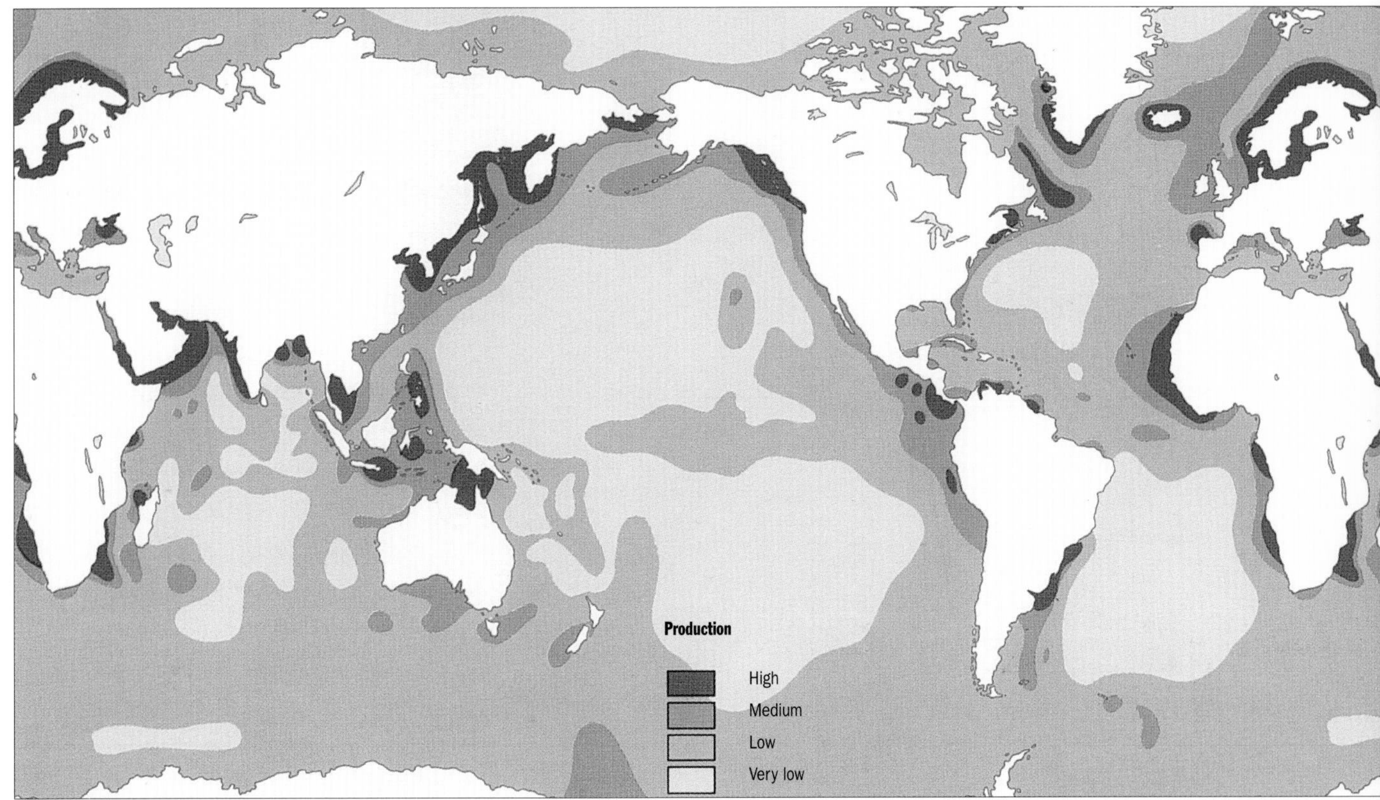

amounts, but those small amounts are essential.

Plant nutrients come mainly from rocks. On land they become part of the soil. As soil they are washed into rivers and carried to the coast. It is around coasts, therefore, that plant nutrients are most abundant. Members of the plankton have no choice where they go, but they thrive and are numerous only where conditions are favorable. This means there is much more plankton in coastal waters than there is in the open ocean. Since the plankton forms the basis for the food supply, fish are also most plentiful in coastal waters.

SEAWEEDS

Algae are fairly simple plants that have no true stems, roots, or leaves. They include seaweeds, diatoms (microscopic single-celled algae), and spirogyra (green freshwater multicellular algae). Seaweeds are the largest algae. Having no roots, they absorb the food they need from the water around them, and they live attached to rocks or other solid objects. Some are secured by a "holdfast"—a long, tough, rubbery structure terminating in a disk with suckers.

Seaweeds grow only in relatively shallow water, different types occurring at different depths. Some of the largest seaweeds, called kelps, grow in large numbers, often forming extensive "forests," their fronds swaying with the movement of the water.

Like a forest on land, the kelp forests provide food and shelter for a large variety of animals. Some live on the bottom or burrow below it. The fish float effortlessly among the kelp fronds.

PHYTOPLANKTON COVERAGE. Phytoplankton is the plant constituent of plankton, the organisms inhabiting the upper layer of a sea. Phytoplankton floats near the surface, where sunlight can reach it, but the tiny plants also require other nutrients that are not available everywhere. The map shows that phytoplankton is most abundant near coasts, where rivers carry plant nutrients washed from the land.

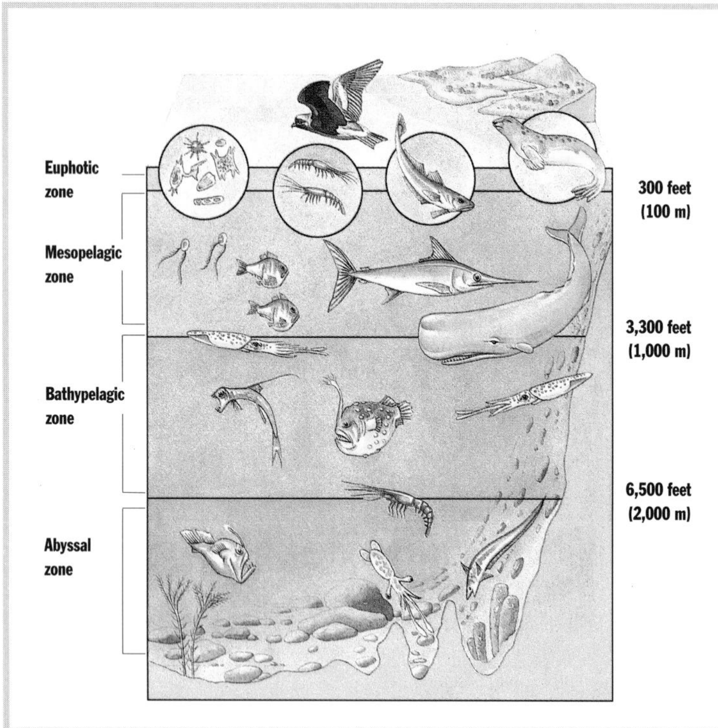

OCEAN ZONES. The ocean becomes deeper with increasing distance from the coast. Light, necessary for photosynthesis, penetrates only to the bottom of the euphotic zone. In cloudy coastal waters the depth of the euphotic zone may be only 100 feet (30 m). Beneath it the ocean is divided horizontally into zones on the basis of the animals living there.

OCEAN ZONES

Continents do not end abruptly where land and sea meet. At the edge of the sea the shore slopes downward quite gently. It is not until you are about 200 miles (320 km) from land that you reach the deep ocean.

Imagine you have some kind of submarine car in which you can drive along the sea floor. As you move away from the shore, you will drive about 60 miles (100 km) down a very gradual slope. This is called the continental shelf. At the end of it the slope steepens. This is where sediments washed down by rivers onto the shelf slide off the edge. It is called the continental slope and continues for about 30 miles (50 km) before almost leveling out into a very long, much more gentle descent. This is the continental rise, and when you have driven across it for about 125 miles (200 km), you will reach the real ocean floor, called the abyssal plain.

Denizens of the Deep

As you move deeper into the sea, it grows dark rather quickly. Near the coast, where sediment clouds the water, you will pass the last of the plants at a depth of about 100 feet (30 m), although this region, called the euphotic zone, continues to about 300 feet (100 m) in the clearer water of the open sea. Below that it is too dark for photosynthesis, and you enter what is called the mesopelagic zone.

This is a darker world, but not an empty one. Many fish inhabit it, some spending most of their time in it, others diving for food then returning to shallower depths. Whales swim in this zone.

Below about 3,300 feet (1,000 m) you enter the bathypelagic zone, a region of total darkness inhabited by animals adapted to survive on only an occasional meal—which means it has to be a big one. Giant squid swim at this depth, and sperm whales hunt them.

Many of the deep-water fishes have the property of bioluminescence—the ability to produce light themselves—and they appear in various patterns and colors. The light is used for recognition (for the sexes to find one another and to allow fish to travel in schools), to lure prey, and to ward off enemies.

There is deeper water yet. At about 6,500 feet (2,000 m) you enter the abyssal zone. Now more than a mile of water separates you from

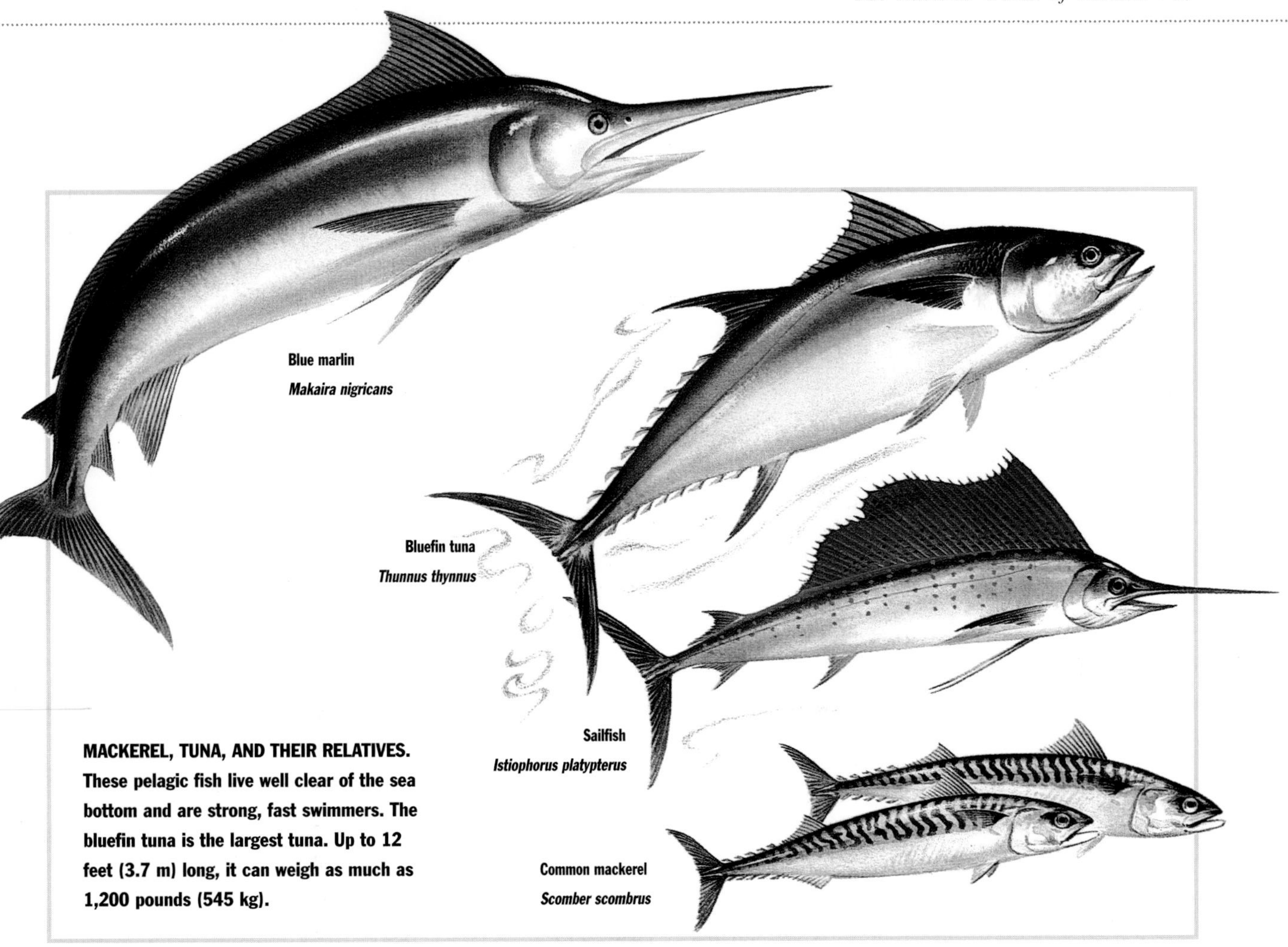

MACKEREL, TUNA, AND THEIR RELATIVES. These pelagic fish live well clear of the sea bottom and are strong, fast swimmers. The bluefin tuna is the largest tuna. Up to 12 feet (3.7 m) long, it can weigh as much as 1,200 pounds (545 kg).

the sunlit surface. Strange, fanlike animals that look like plants rise above the surface of the mud and sand, but there are very few of them. Small, shrimp-like animals pass you, and you may see a deep-sea angler fish waiting for a meal to come within reach of its immense mouth. At the abyssal level as many as 44 percent of the fish may be light producers.

Over most of the ocean this is the bottom, but there are still deeper places. Ocean trenches, where one tectonic plate is being subducted beneath its neighbor, are the deepest places on the surface of the planet. The deepest of them lies near the Philippines. It is called the Marianas Trench, and it is 36,000 feet (11,000 m) deep.

PELAGIC FISH

The familiar fish—the ones we see in aquariums and that are shaped like torpedoes—are strong swimmers. They are called pelagic. This means they live in the open sea well clear of the bottom, in "mid-water." Their travels between the regions where they feed and those where they breed can take them thousands of miles.

Mackerel and tuna are typical pelagic fish. Both belong to the same family (Scombridae). They live in large groups called shoals, are fast swimmers, and feed on fish smaller than themselves. They are also hunted by bigger fish and by mammals such as dolphins—and humans. Many are commercially valuable, especially the bluefin tuna (*Thunnus thynnus*), albacore (*Thunnus alalunga*), and mackerel (*Scomber scombrus*). Herrings (*Clupea harengula*) and pilchards (*Sardinia pilchardus*)—called sardines when they are small—are also pelagic species.

It is not only fish that live in the surface waters. So do some reptiles. Sea snakes are not mythical beasts—they really exist. Many snakes enter the sea from time to time, but two subfamilies (Hydrophinae and Laticaudinae) related to the cobras live there permanently. The Laticaudinae go ashore to lay their eggs, but the Hydrophinae produce live young in the water. All sea snakes are venomous and feed on fish.

INVERTEBRATES

Invertebrates (animals lacking a backbone) of the sea include some of the strangest sea creatures: sponges, Portuguese man-of-war, jellyfish, corals, and anemones.

Most animals possess body organs, such as a stomach and heart. Sponges do not. They live attached to a solid surface, most of them in the sea, and they have no organs. Instead, they have cells that fan water along a network of canals, opening through pores at the body surface. Many of them have an outer covering, like a skin, and a skeleton made of tiny spikes of a hard mineral to keep the canals open.

If a sponge seems strange, the Portuguese man-of-war (*Physalia physalis*) is even stranger. It looks like a jellyfish, but in fact it is a community of very small animals, some called polyps, others medusae, and all of them modified to perform particular functions. One medusa with the form of a big bag of gas acts as a float. A fringe on the top forms a sail, and other medusae at the bottom are able to swim, propelling the colony through the water. Some of the polyps catch small animals using long tentacles spread out like a net and armed with stinging cells that inject poison into their prey, and other polyps eat them. Some specialize in reproduction.

Jellyfish and Polyps

Jellyfish have gelatinous, umbrella-shaped bodies with trailing, stinging tentacles.

A jellyfish is a medusa, but not a colony like the Portuguese man-of-war. A medusa and a polyp are different stages in the life cycle of the same animal. The polyp is like a tiny tube, with one end sealed where it is attached to a surface and with a mouth surrounded by tentacles at the other end. It stays in one place, but a medusa grows on its side and then detaches itself. The medusa swims away, mates with another medusa, and lays eggs. These grow into larvae that swim freely for a time then turn into polyps.

Although this is a general pattern, many of these animals have given up one or the other stage, so they spend all their lives as polyps or as medusae. The jellyfish you meet at sea have given up being polyps, for example.

Many polyps protect their soft bodies with a shell of calcium carbonate, and many live in large colonies. Some of these form coral reefs. Others grow as delicate fans or as treelike forms.

INVERTEBRATES OF THE NORTH ATLANTIC. The Portuguese man-of-war and jellyfish hunt small animals by means of long tentacles bearing cells, called nematocysts, that shoot out threads that sting prey. *Obelia geniculata* is a hydroid, a colony of polyps. So are *Sertularia operculata*, dead man's fingers, and the sea fan. All of these are varieties of coral. There are many species of sea anemone, animals with stinging tentacles around their mouths.

Sea Anemones

Sea anemones are polyps that look like plants. They are bigger than other polyps. Most are up to about 2 inches (5 cm) long and 0.75 inches (2 cm) to the size of a half dollar across, but there are much smaller and much bigger species.

There are sea anemones more than 3 feet (1 m) in diameter on the northwest coast of the United States. They are found in a bewildering variety of shapes and colors, reflecting the different environments in which they live.

The animal has an almost cylindrical, muscular body. This is firmly attached to a surface by a flat disk. At the other end there is another disk, and at its center a slit-shaped mouth. Tentacles surround the mouth. Some species have just a few tentacles, others hundreds, and many carry stinging cells. While the animal is feeding, its tentacles feel for prey—and large anemones can capture small fish.

At other times, especially at low tide or when the delicate tentacles might be damaged, anemones "shut down;" they draw in their tentacles and close the disk over them.

Some anemones live on the shells of hermit crabs. They feed on particles of food and protect the crab from predators.

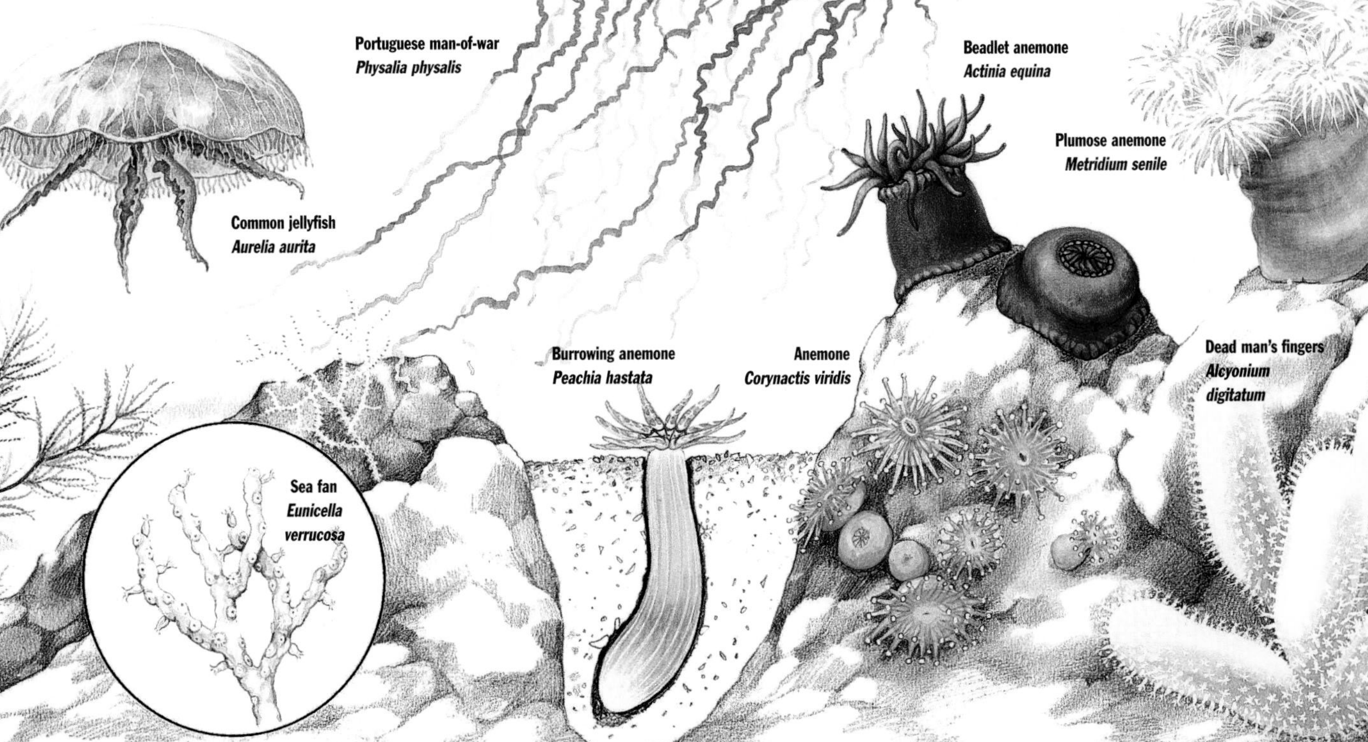

INSECTS OF THE SEA

Arthropods have hard skeletons outside their bodies. On land we know them as insects, spiders, scorpions, centipedes, and similar animals. Those that live in the sea are called crustaceans. Lobsters, crayfish, crabs, prawns, and shrimps are crustaceans and so are barnacles. The crustaceans are sometimes referred to as "insects of the sea." Altogether there are probably more than 25,000 species.

They vary greatly in size. The biggest is probably the Japanese, or giant, spider crab (*Macrocheira kaempferi*). Its longest limbs—those with the claws—are more than 6 feet (1.8 m) long. The smallest is probably *Parabathynella neotropica*, which looks a bit like a centipede and is 0.05 inches (1.2 mm) long.

Most crustaceans feed partly as scavengers, on dead animals, and partly as predators, especially of invertebrates such as shellfish, which they have no difficulty opening with their powerful claws. The mantis shrimps, for example, are fierce predators.

Some crustaceans and fish "clean" parasites from other animals, benefiting both themselves and their hosts.

Many crustaceans are food for other animals and, of course, we eat some ourselves. The edible crab, lobster, and crayfish are popular. Scampi, a popular European food, is the tail of the Norway lobster (*Nephrops norvegicus*). Other crustaceans, shrimplike animals called krill (*Euphausia superba*), are the main food for whales. (A blue whale can eat about 1 ton, 907 kg, of them in a meal and often eats four meals a day.) Krill are about 2 inches (5 cm) long and almost transparent. In the Southern Ocean there are vast shoals of krill, often with up to 75,000 per square yard (63,000 per sq. m).

Mantis shrimp
***Squilla* species**

Cleaner shrimp
Hippolysmata grabhami

Tropical shrimp
Periclimones imperator

SPECIES OF SHRIMP. Most shrimps live in the sea, although there are some freshwater species. The three species shown above all live in tropical waters. The cleaner shrimp is so called because it uses its mouthparts to remove parasites from the skin of fish. Here it is shown with a butterfly fish.

ON THE SEA BED

Fish that live near the sea bed, feeding on invertebrate animals such as worms, are called

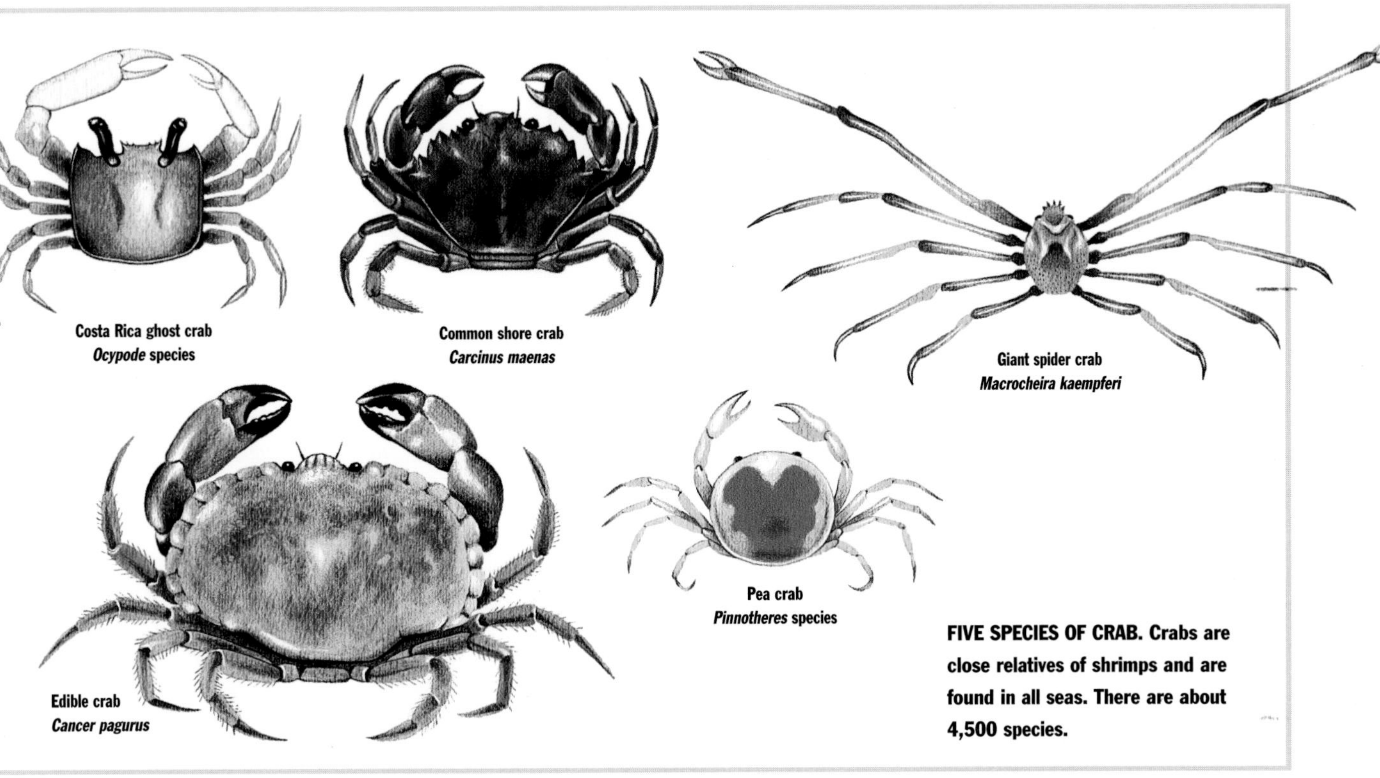

FIVE SPECIES OF CRAB. Crabs are close relatives of shrimps and are found in all seas. There are about 4,500 species.

demersal. Some demersal fish are streamlined, like pelagic fish, and swim strongly. Cod (*Gadus morrhua* in the North Atlantic and *G. macrocephalus* in the North Pacific), haddock (*Melanogrammus aeglefinus*), and hake (*Merluccius merluccius* in the North Atlantic and *M. productus* in the Pacific) are demersal fish.

Flatfish

Some fish live right at the bottom of shallow seas, spending much of their time half buried in the sand or mud. Until they move, they are almost invisible. To help them hide their bodies, they are flattened. The halibut (*Hippoglossus hippoglossus*), Greenland halibut (*Reinhardtius hippoglossoides*), Californian halibut (*Paralichthys californicus*), and European turbot (*Scophthalmus maximus*) are all flatfish.

As a larva and young fish, a flatfish lives as part of the plankton and looks just like a tiny but ordinary fish with a torpedo-shaped body. As it grows bigger, however, its body starts to change. It begins to grow more and more disk-shaped and one of its eyes starts to move across the top of its head until both eyes are on the same side. Then the fish turns onto its side, so its eyes are on top; it lives this way for the rest of its life.

Flatfish have eyes on either their left or right sides. The Greenland halibut and flounder (*Platichthys flesus*) are right-eye fish, the European turbot and Californian halibut are left-eye fish.

The fish are usually pale on their undersides, but on top they are so well camouflaged they blend with the sand or stones among which they live. Some of them are able to change color to match their background. Plaice (*Pleuronectes platessa*) and its relatives are especially good at this. Some can even blend with a checkered background.

DEEP-SEA FISH that hunt in mid-water cannot afford to miss the chance of a meal, because the deep ocean is sparsely populated and prey is hard to find. Their fearsome teeth and jaws are necessary for their survival.

TERRORS OF THE DEEP

Sharks have a fearsome reputation. It is true that some are dangerous to humans, but most are not. All sharks are predators, and some feed on invertebrates they gather on the sea bed. Angelsharks, for example, have broad bodies, rather like rays, and spend much of their time half buried in the sand or mud. They occur in most temperate and tropical waters, but not in the central Pacific or the Indian Ocean. Their diet comprises crustaceans and mollusks including squid and octopuses, as well as small fish. Wobbegongs, found off Australia and New Guinea, feed in the same way, as do blind sharks, also found off Australian coasts, and the most widely distributed bullhead sharks. The biggest of all fishes is the whale shark (*Rhiniodon typus*). It grows to 40 feet (12 m), lives in warm waters, and feeds mainly on plankton, although it will take small fish. The basking shark (*Cetorhinus maximus*) grows to 33 feet (10 m) or sometimes rather more. It is found throughout the North and South Atlantic and Pacific Oceans and it, too, feeds on plankton.

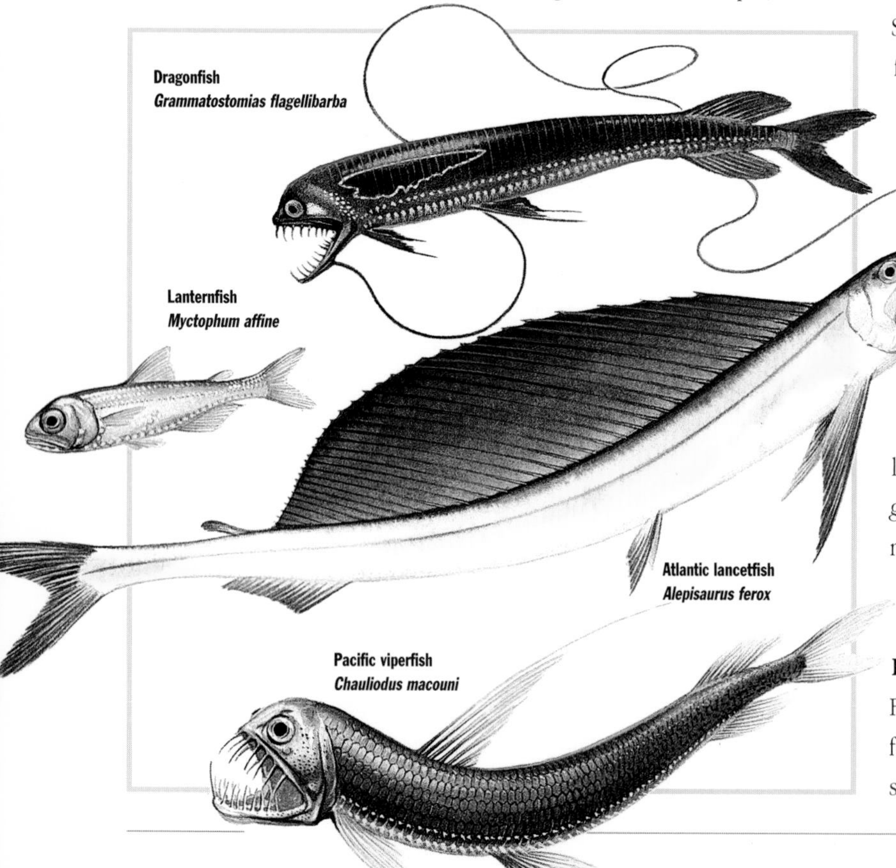

Apart from the whale and basking sharks most of these sharks are fairly small. Some will attack divers if they are provoked or threatened, but they are not naturally aggressive. Sharks that attack humans are much bigger. They are aggressive, and some of them hunt in shallow water. The bullshark (*Carcharinus leucas*) grows to more than 11 feet (3.4 m) long, the related Galápagos shark (*C. galapagensis*) grows to 12 feet (3.6 m), and the most famous of all, the great white shark (*Carcharodon carcharias*), to 20 feet (6 m).

Eternal Darkness and Cold

Far below the sunlit world of coral reefs, kelp forests, and large shoals of fish—the world of the sharks—there is another world. There, no light

THE GREAT WHITE SHARK grows up to 20 feet (6 m) long and is a formidable predator. It feeds mainly on fish, but it also takes dolphins, porpoises, and seals. Occasionally, great white sharks attack people.

penetrates. The darkness is total. And it is cold. No matter how warm the water may be at the surface, below about 1,000 feet (300 m) the temperature falls rapidly with increasing depth. At about 3,300 feet (1,000 m) it is about 41°F (5°C) in all oceans, and at 13,000 feet (4,000 m) it is 34–36°F (1–2°C).

There is life even there, in the eternal darkness and cold. Sea spiders, which look like spiders but are only very distant relatives of the spiders that live on land, are among the deep-sea inhabitants. They have been found in the Japan Trench at a depth of 24,181 feet (7,370 m). There are crabs, prawns, and animals resembling lobsters down to about 14,765 feet (4,500 m), although some of them do not look much like their shallow-water cousins.

If the crustaceans look strange, some of the fish are much more bizarre and terrifying until you realize they are not very big. Many of the 220 or so species of lanternfish are only about 4 inches (10 cm) long. Even the most alarming of the deep-sea fish are small. Sloane's viperfish (*Chauliodus sloani*) is only 1 foot (30 cm) long, and it is the largest of the six species of viperfish. The gulper eel (*Eurypharynx pelecanoides*) is much longer, growing to 24 inches (60 cm), and the snipe eels (*Nemichthys* species) are even bigger, some reaching 4 feet (1.2 m), but these are both eels and most of their length is tail. There are exceptions. Saccopharynx eels (family Saccopharyngidae) can be up to 5.6 feet (1.7 m) long, and the Atlantic lancetfish (*Alepisaurus ferox*) grows to 6 feet (1.8 m).

Melanocoetus

Edriolynchus

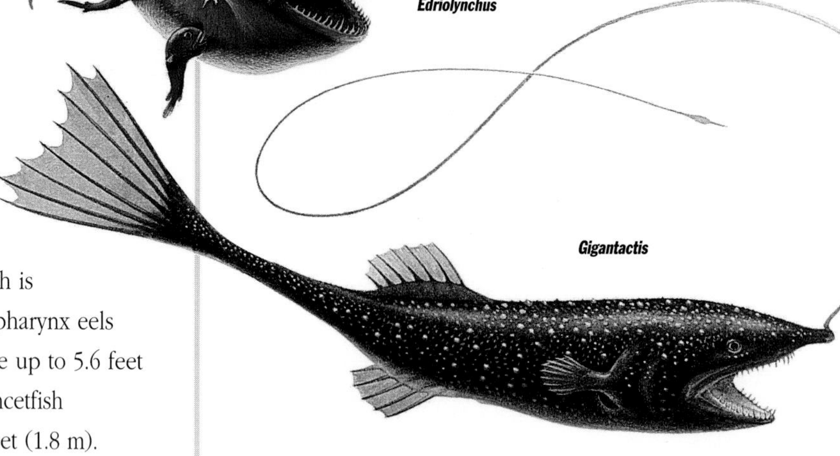

Gigantactis

Deep-sea fish are small because their habitat supplies them with insufficient food to sustain a bigger body. The lancetfish is larger because it is a voracious predator and its prey consists of the smaller deep-sea fishes. The length of saccopharynx eels consists mainly of tail.

Size apart, the most conspicuous feature of these fish is their mouths and teeth. Most of them have immense mouths, with long, sharp teeth that are often curved. Some, including the viperfish, have no floor to their mouths. They can swing their jaws upward, out of the way, revealing a second set of teeth in the pharynx at the entrance to the throat. It is as though they had two mouths, one behind the other.

These arrangements have evolved in a region where meals are few and far between. When a deep-sea predator meets its prey, it must eat all of it, and it must do so immediately, because another fish may arrive at any moment to steal any food that is not devoured at once. That is why these fish have such huge mouths. Many of them can swallow prey larger than themselves, their bodies stretching to accommodate the meal. Swinging the jaws out of the way is another means to the same end. There are no bones in the pharynx, which means that it can expand.

ANGLER FISH

There are about 215 species of angler fish. Not all of them inhabit deep water, but they all live on or near the ocean floor where food is scarce. Most anglers have the first fin ray of the dorsal

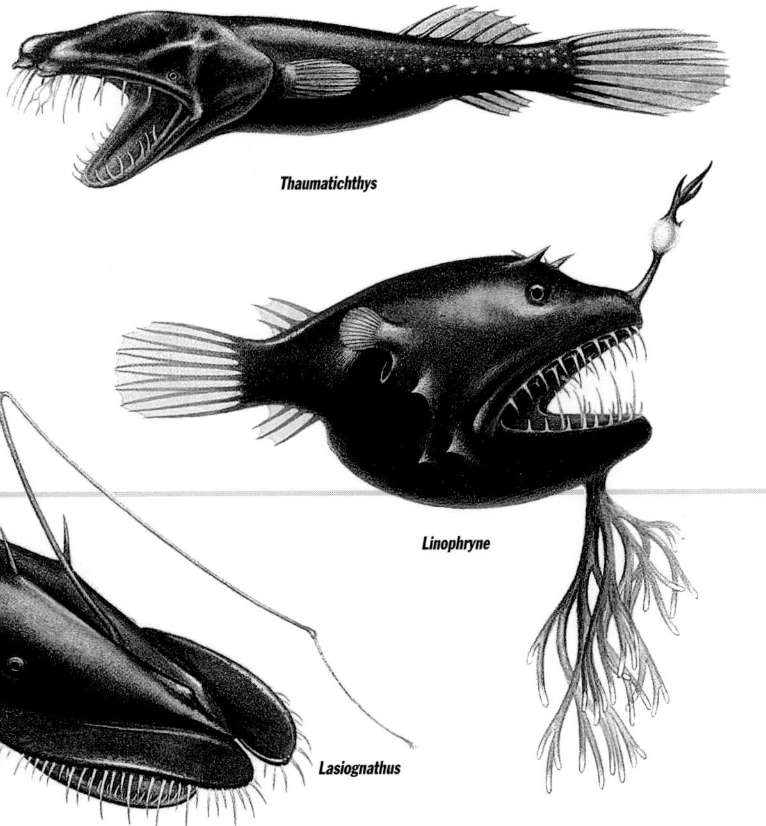

DEEP-SEA ANGLER FISH have a modified spiny dorsal fin with which to lure their prey. They look terrifying, but the biggest is no more than 6 inches (15 cm) long, and most are only 3 inches (7 cm) long.

fin modified into a "fishing pole," called an illicium, with a small flap of skin at its end as a lure. The fish dangles the lure in front of its huge mouth, waving the flap of skin slowly in the water so it looks like a morsel of food. Any fish that comes too close is seized. Lures are sometimes elaborate. *Linophryne arborifera* is typical of a deep-sea species found in the Atlantic, Pacific, and Indian Oceans. Its lure looks like a bit of seaweed, and it has another, bigger piece of "seaweed" below its mouth. It is a fearsome-looking animal, but measures barely 3 inches (7 cm) from nose to tail.

Males That Are Parasites

Deep-sea fish face another problem—finding mates. Bioluminescence (see page 16) is one adaption to this problem.

Some of the anglers, including *Linophryne arborifera*, however, have developed another unique solution. Their larvae start life looking much like any other fish larvae, but as they grow bigger, males start to change. They grow much more slowly than the females and develop pincer-like teeth. By the time they mature sexually, the females are up to 20 times bigger than the males. The males then attach themselves to the females, the tissues of the two fish merge, and the male becomes nothing more than a set of reproductive organs, living the rest of its life as a parasite.

MAMMALS OF THE SEA: WHALES

Whales are mammals, which means that they are warm-blooded and nurse their young. (Other mammals that live in the sea include seals, sea lions, and manatees.) They live in every ocean of the world.

Whales are descended from animals that evolved on land then returned to live in the sea. Once back in the sea, the fish-eating ancestors of modern whales gained a tremendous advantage—they became weightless. This allowed them to become very large and still

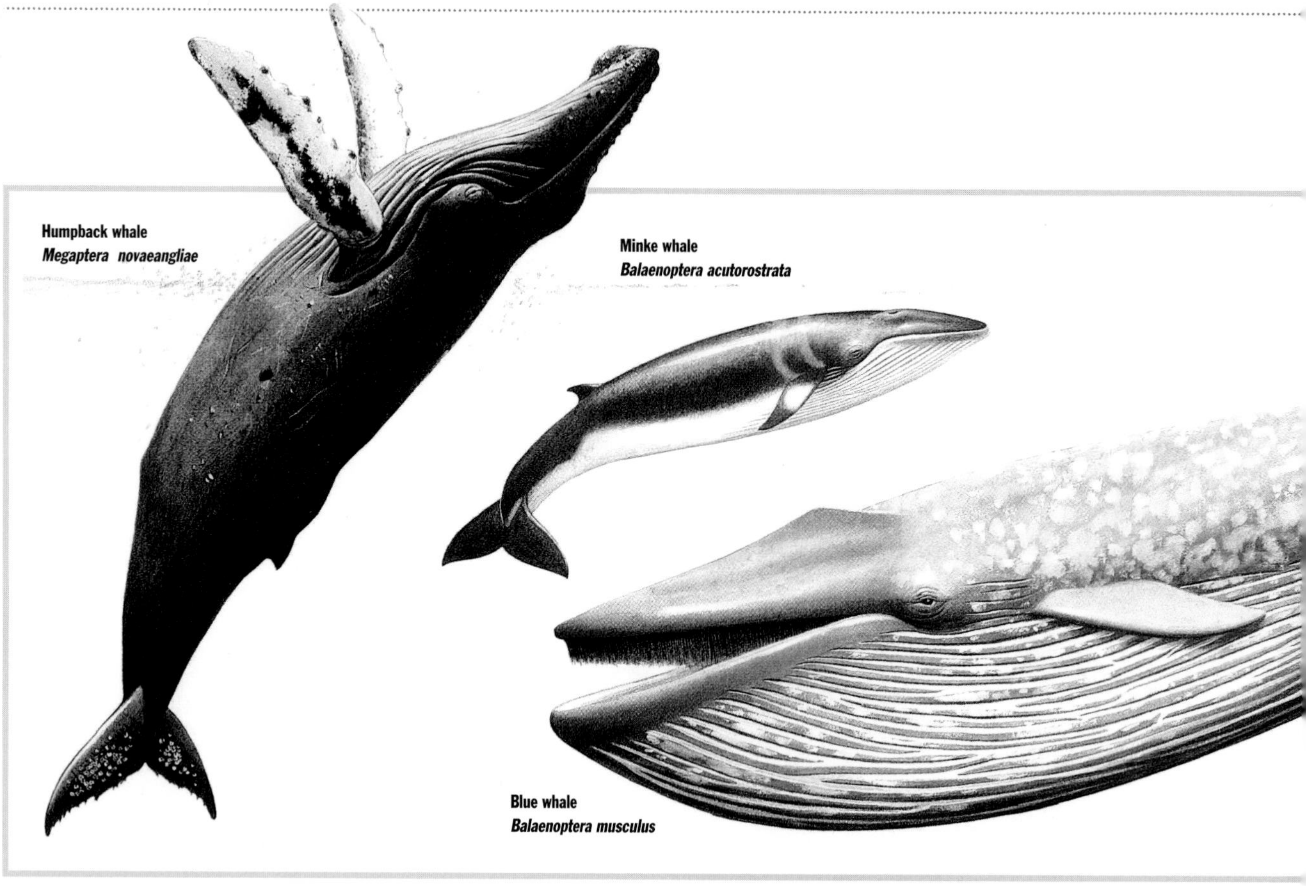

Humpback whale
Megaptera novaeangliae

Minke whale
Balaenoptera acutorostrata

Blue whale
Balaenoptera musculus

BALEEN WHALES. The humpback whale is shown in the attitude it adopts when "singing" its famous "song." The minke is one of the smaller whales; its numbers have increased and in some areas it is now abundant. The blue whale is the largest living creature on Earth; it can grow to more than 100 feet (33 m) long. The gray whale shown here is a female with young. It is found in the Pacific Ocean. The fin whale lives in the Arctic, where it is still hunted.

move around. Being large, in turn, allowed them to withstand the cold.

Being warm-blooded, whales can control their body temperatures. Like other mammals and birds, they generate heat by converting food to energy. Water conducts heat much faster than air so it is much harder to keep warm in the sea than on land. Whales overcame the problem of keeping warm by acquiring a thick layer of body fat, called blubber, and by their size. A larger body mass helps because the amount of heat generated is greater, and larger animals have a smaller surface area in relation to their volume. The outcome of this adaptation is that whales represent some of the largest animals on Earth.

Whales have lungs and breathe through blowholes; they can hold their breath only for short periods, but when they fill their lungs, nearly all the air they take in is new. Some whales can stay underwater for as long as 45 minutes.

Some species of whales undertake long migrations, making annual trips between the poles and the equator. Blue whales spend the summer in Arctic or Antarctic waters, where krill is most abundant. In winter they move to equatorial waters, where they mate.

One population of gray whales (family Eschrichtidae) spends the summer feeding in the Sea of Okhotsk and the winter in the East China Sea. The other population spends summer in the Bering Sea and the winter off Baja California 12,500 miles (20,000 km) away.

There are two suborders in the order Cetacea, which includes all whales. The Mysticeti comprises the ten species of baleen whales,

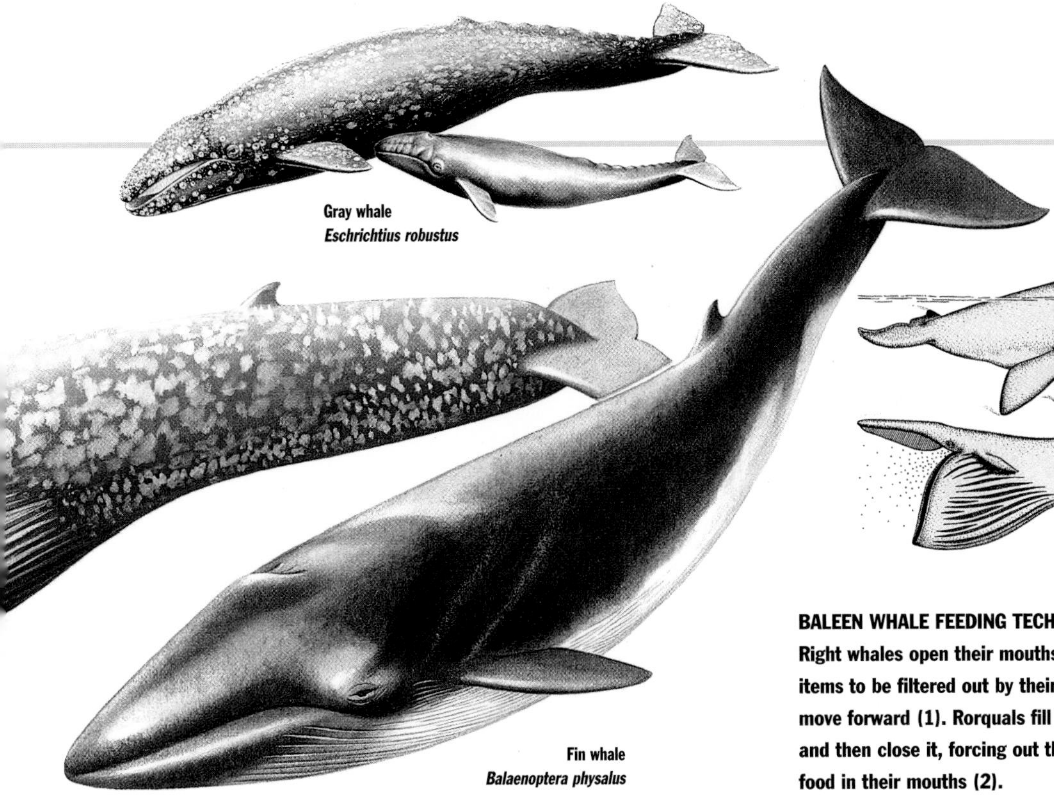

Gray whale
Eschrichtius robustus

1

2

Fin whale
Balaenoptera physalus

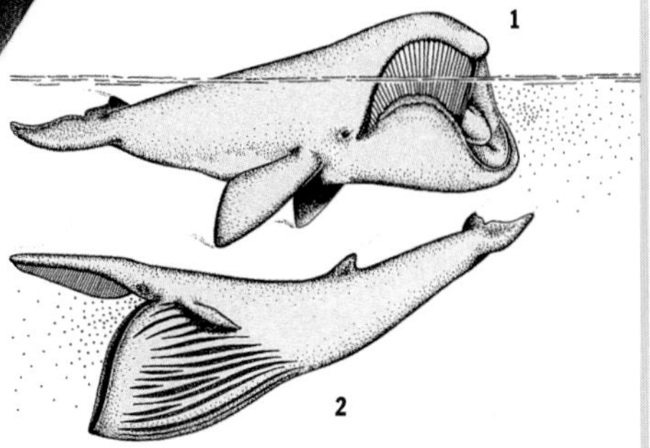

BALEEN WHALE FEEDING TECHNIQUES.
Right whales open their mouths wide to allow food items to be filtered out by their baleen plates as they move forward (1). Rorquals fill their mouths with water and then close it, forcing out the water and leaving the food in their mouths (2).

which do not have teeth. These include the blue, humpback, and gray whales. The Odontoceti, or toothed whales, comprises 66 species. These include white whales, sperm whales, dolphins, and porpoises. Both groups are descended from a common ancestor.

BALEEN WHALES

When they are young, baleen whales have rudimentary teeth. They lose these as they grow older and develop the adult feeding apparatus of baleen plates. These are made from keratin and hang from the roof of the mouth. The whale swims along slowly with its immense mouth wide open. Water, together with all the tiny animals living in it, enters the mouth. The baleen

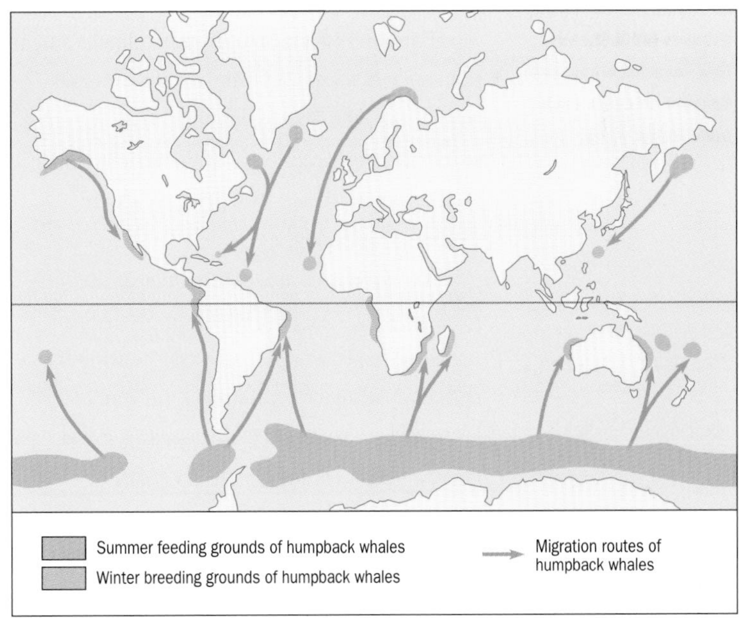

MIGRATION PATTERNS OF HUMPBACK WHALES. The map shows the routes followed by humpback whales between their feeding and breeding grounds.

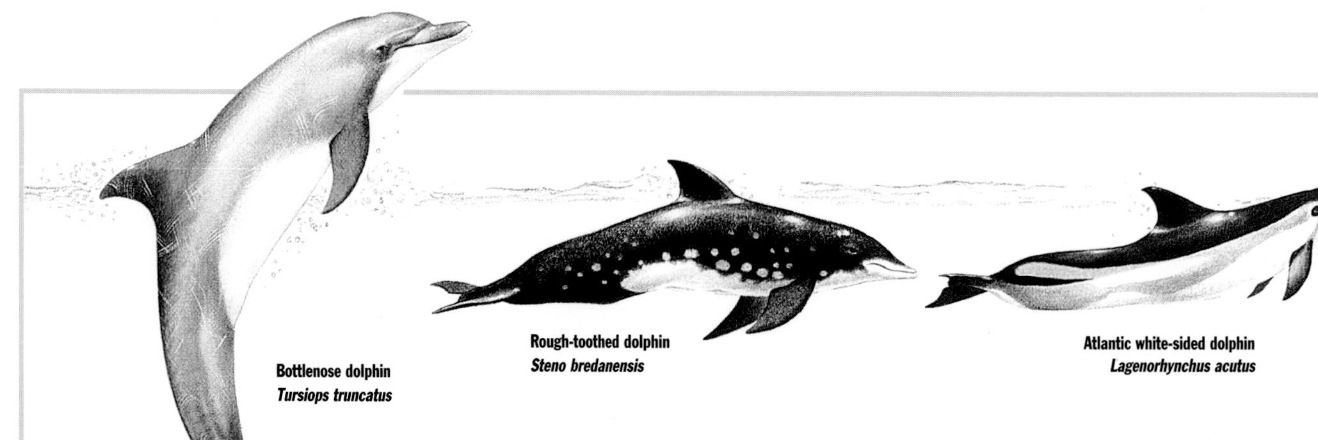

DOLPHINS. The bottlenose dolphin, with its characteristic "smile," is the most familiar to humans. The agility and playfulness of dolphins have endeared them to people. Their graceful leaps seem to be simply for fun. Dusky dolphins are known for their amazing leaps, and they like to chase each other in the water.

plates trap the animals, and the whale pushes out the water through the sides of its mouth. The rorquals—the family (Balaenopteridae) that includes the minke, blue, sei, and humpback whales—do this by closing the mouth. Food is trapped in the baleen fringes, and the whale uses its tongue to wipe the food to the back of its mouth to be swallowed.

The number and size of baleen plates vary from species to species. Minkes, for example, have about 300. They reach their most extreme size in the bowhead, or Greenland right, whale (*Balaena mysticetus*). Its baleen plates are 15 feet (4.5 m) long.

Baleen whales are quite particular about what they eat. The gray whale (*Eschrichtius robustus*) feeds on the sea bottom, stirring up mud with its snout and filtering the water for invertebrates. Humpback whales (*Megaptera novaeangliae*) eat krill in the Southern Hemisphere and small fish in the Northern. The blue whale, along with several other whales, prefers krill.

Whales communicate in a variety of sounds, including whistles, chirps, and lower-pitched noises, but humpback whales in particular are famous for the "singing" noises they make in communication. (The sounds are produced by the movement of air through their blowholes.) They can call to each other over distances of thousands of miles.

TOOTHED WHALES

In all there are 66 species of toothed whales. These include sperm whales and white whales, a group that comprises the beluga and the narwhal whale. There are also beaked whales (which are seldom seen), porpoises, dolphins, and river dolphins—freshwater dolphins that are found in South America and Asia.

Sperm whales are the largest of the whales with teeth. The best-known sperm whale is *Physeter catodon*. It varies in length from 36 to 66 feet (11 to 20 m), and its huge head accounts for one-third of its length. This contains a mass of a waxy substance called spermaceti, which is believed to help it control its buoyancy. Sperm whales are known to dive to 6,500 feet (2,000 m) in search of food and are often heavily scarred from encounters with giant squid. These whales

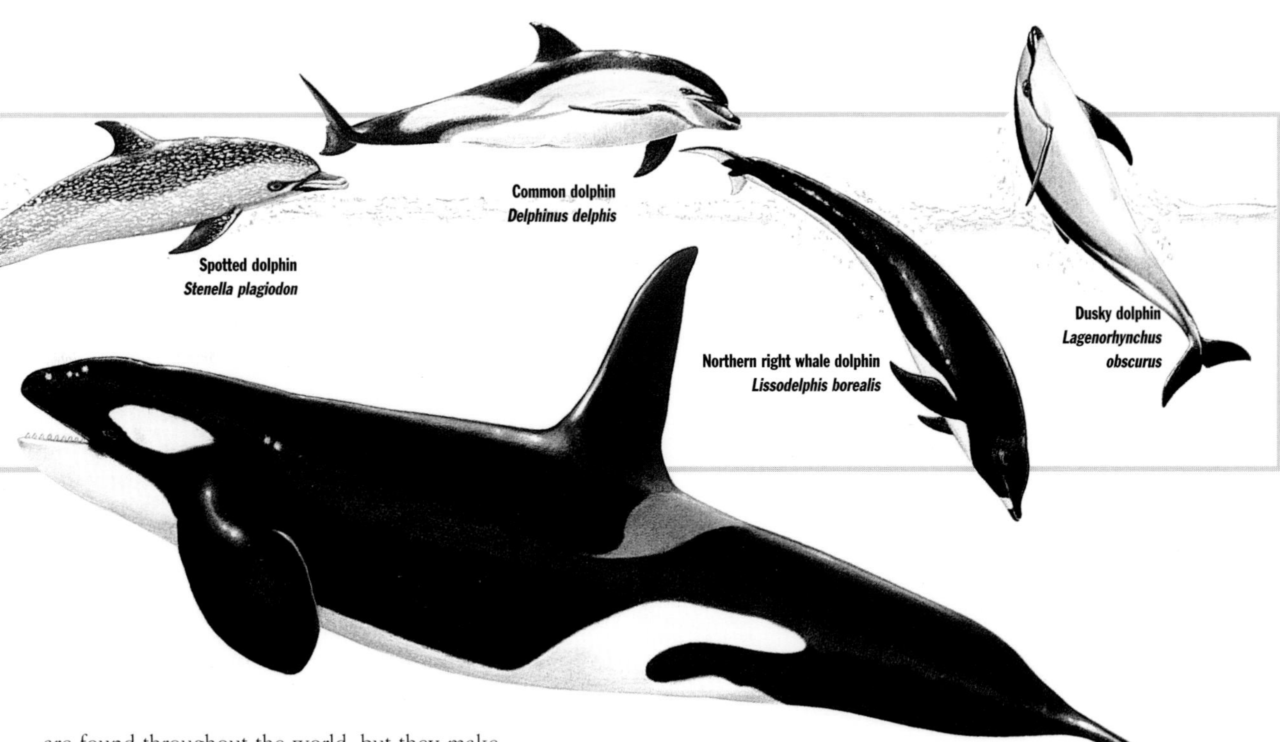

are found throughout the world, but they make regular migrations to the Southern Ocean in pursuit of the squid.

The narwhal (*Monodon monoceros*) inhabits Arctic waters. The male narwhal has a long tusk that is actually the upper left incisor tooth, which grows through the lip and can be up to 9 feet (2.7 m) long.

Dolphins

Dolphins are small whales, usually with a beaklike snout. They often lack teeth in their upper jaw. They are fast swimmers, making repeated shallow dives and surfacing to breathe.

Dolphins communicate in clicks, squeaks, and whistles similar to the sounds made by some whales. Scientists are still trying to understand more about this communication. Together with some toothed whales, they also make clicking sounds to locate prey and other whales. Sound travels through the water and bounces off objects, as an echo, providing them with feedback on the distance and location of objects. The process is called echolocation. The protruberance on the head of dolphins and some toothed whales, called a melon, is a pad of fat that seems to "focus" the sound. They can also emit a narrow beam of extremely high- or low-pitched sound that stuns fish.

Dolphins are known for their intelligence, playfulness, and amenability toward humans. The species that has been trained to perform in marine parks and in movies is the bottlenose dolphin (*Tursiops truncatus*). Its characteristic "smile" as a result of the curvature of its mouth enhances our identification with these dolphins.

Dolphin groups have a well organized social structure. Bottlenose dolphins live in groups of about 15 individuals, groups sometimes joining together in larger numbers, and individuals are very communicative with each other.

THE KILLER WHALE *(Orcinus orca)*, or orca, is the largest of the dolphin family, growing to a length of 33 feet (10 m). Swift, strong, and armed with 40 to 50 teeth, it is a powerful hunter, feeding on squid, fish, birds, seals, and whales smaller than itself. Killer whales are found in all oceans, especially in cooler waters. Despite their name, and unlike some sharks, they pose little threat to humans.

Common dolphins (*Delphinus delphis*), along with some other species, enjoy swimming alongside moving ships and riding the waves created by their bows. They live in groups of up to 100 or more individuals. These are the dolphins of ancient stories that supposedly went to the aid of humans lost at sea.

Dolphins sometimes collaborate with each other in hunting. They will drive shoals of fish into a bay where the water is shallow and from which there is no escape. This behavior happens so regularly in some places that local fishing communities take advantage of it, waiting for the dolphins then catching some of the fish.

Dolphins are often called porpoises. However, the two are different. Porpoises are whales of the family Phocoenidae. They are seldom more than 7 feet (2.1 m) long and have no "beak." They are sometimes attacked by dolphins. Apart from the spectacled porpoise (*Phocoena dioptrica*), found off the coast of South America, porpoises occur only in the Northern Hemisphere.

The Killer Whale

The killer whale (*Orcinus orca*) is the largest of the dolphin family. It can grow to a length of about 33 feet (10 m) and is recognizable by its striking black-and-white coloring and large dorsal fin. Killer whales travel in groups called pods. A pod is an extended family, and its members—up to 40—stay together for life.

Killer whales feed on squid and fish, but they also eat birds, seals, and other dolphins. Their hunting success is due to their skilled collaboration. This is learned. All adults take part in the hunt while the young imitate them.

One whale of the group is often vertical in the water, with its head above the surface. It is "spy-hopping," watching for those telltale movements that give away the location of a fish shoal. The whales drive their prey into a trap, using underwater sounds to help, then feed at their leisure. They can dislodge a seal from an ice floe by rocking the ice until it turns over.

MIGRATING BIRDS

Like the sea, the air presents no boundaries. Birds make the longest migration of any animal, and many birds undertake journeys every bit as impressive as those made by whales.

Arctic terns (*Sterna paradisaea*) breed in northern Canada during the summer, then move south for the winter. They fly over the Atlantic, some stopping when they reach South Africa, others when they reach South America, but some fly all the way to Antarctica. There it is summer, of course, and they spend it feeding before returning all the way to Canada.

Albatross Gliders

A few albatrosses live in the North Pacific, but most are found only in the Southern Hemisphere. They are big birds, with an average wingspan of about 10 feet (3 m).

Their narrow wings are ideal for gliding, so an albatross flies apparently effortlessly. It exploits the fact that in a boundary layer close to the sea surface friction slows the wind, so the wind is slower there than it is at a higher level. The bird loses height gliding downwind, and when it is almost touching the water, it turns into

MIGRATION ROUTES of Arctic terns *(Sterna paradisaea) (map, right)*. These birds breed in northern Canada and Eurasia. The Canadian population then heads south, some of them all the way to the Southern Ocean, off the coast of Antarctica, often circling it before returning along their original tracks.

MIGRATION of the slender-billed, or short-tailed, shearwater *(Puffinus tenuirostris) (map, right)*. In September it leaves Alaska, heading for California. From there, in October it crosses the open sea to Australia, arriving in November. It stays there until March, then resumes its journey. It spends April and May flying to Japan and June and August flying over the open sea once more, past the tip of Kamchatka and the Aleutian Islands, arriving in Alaska in September.

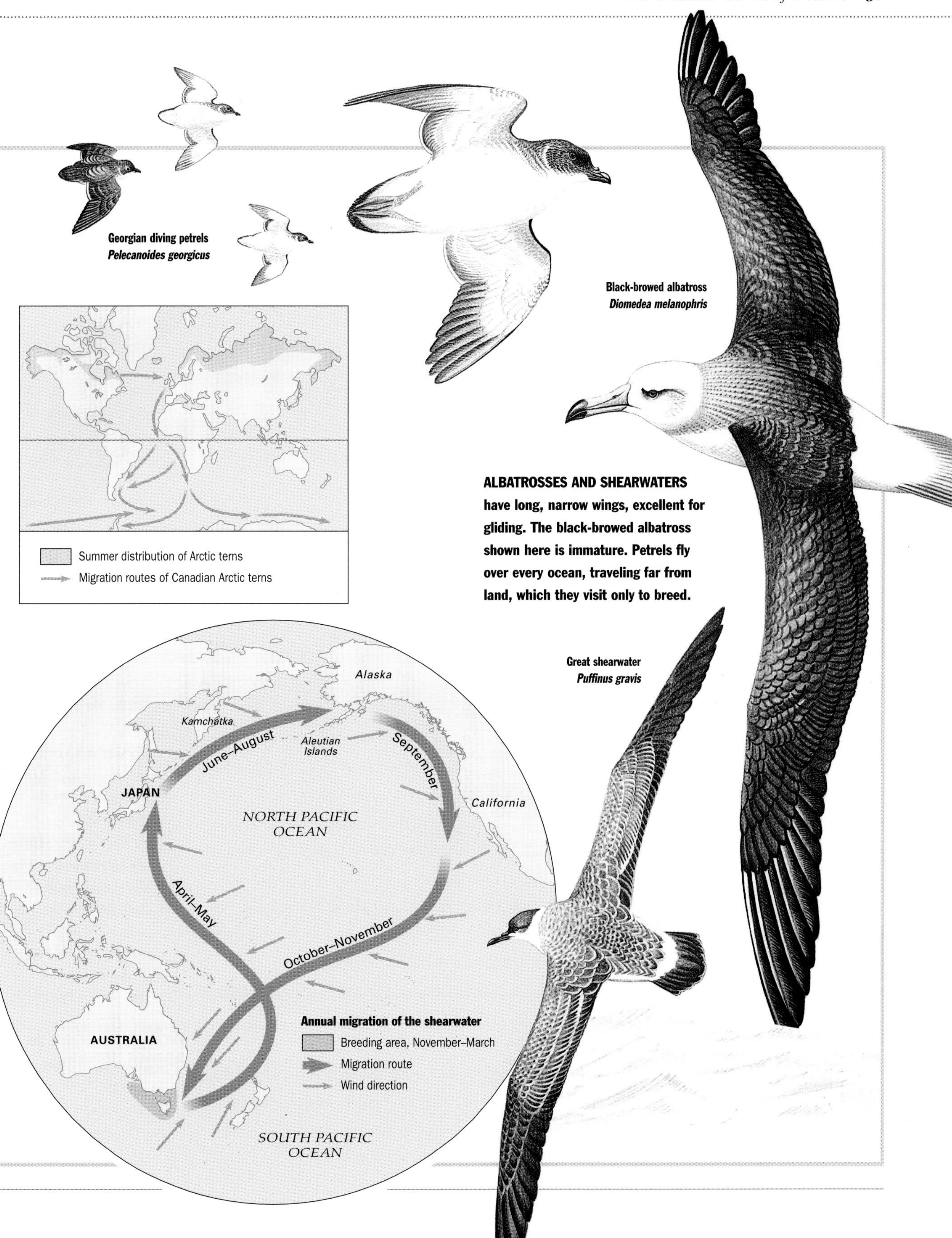

Georgian diving petrels
Pelecanoides georgicus

Black-browed albatross
Diomedea melanophris

Great shearwater
Puffinus gravis

ALBATROSSES AND SHEARWATERS have long, narrow wings, excellent for gliding. The black-browed albatross shown here is immature. Petrels fly over every ocean, traveling far from land, which they visit only to breed.

the wind. This accelerates the airflow across its wings, increasing the lift, so it climbs. As it climbs clear of the boundary layer, the wind speed and therefore the lift increase, so it soars back to its cruising height. Their travels take them immense distances, mainly over the Southern Ocean. They are known for their habit of following ships.

Other Long-Distance Travelers

Shearwaters, fulmars, and petrels belong to the same order (Procellariiformes) as albatrosses. These are smaller birds, although some have a wingspan of 6 feet (1.8 m). They inhabit all oceans, and they, too, undertake long journeys.

The slender-billed, or short-tailed, shearwater (*Puffinus tenuirostris*) circles the Pacific Ocean, following the coast from Alaska to California, crossing the ocean to Australia, flying from there to Japan, then parallel to the Russian coast and across the Bering Sea to Alaska. Its migration takes it 20,000 miles (32,000 km). The Manx, or common, shearwater (*Puffinus puffinus*) has been known to fly from Britain to Australia, and one, taken from Britain and released in Boston, Massachusetts, took less than two weeks to fly back, a distance of 3,000 miles (4,800 km). The greater shearwater (*P. gravis*) breeds early in the year on Tristan da Cunha, in the South Atlantic, then flies north as far as Greenland.

THE SEARCH FOR FOOD

Sea birds feed on plankton, fish, and squid. To do this they have adapted various hunting methods. Georgian diving petrels (*Pelecanoides georgicus*), found near South Georgia in the South Atlantic, fly into the waves to catch krill. Petrels and cormorants swim under water to catch their prey.

Cormorants—Skilled Divers

Cormorants are common in coastal waters and enter estuaries, traveling quite far upstream. The most widely distributed, and the largest, is the common, or great, cormorant (*Phalacrocorax carbo*). Cormorants are strong fliers. They hunt under water and can dive for 20 to 30 seconds, using their webbed feet for propulsion and steering with their tails.

After feeding, cormorants stand with their wings outstretched. This behavior puzzled scientists for a long time—it was assumed the birds were drying their wings (which makes little sense, since the feathers repel water). In fact, they are absorbing the warmth of the sunshine. This speeds up their digestion.

In China fishermen use trained cormorants to catch fish. (The Stuart kings of England also used this method.) The cormorant is released from the boat on a long lead. When it makes a catch, a cord around its throat prevents it from swallowing the fish.

Jaegers—Expert Hunters

When a seabird catches a fish, it usually eats it at once, but during the breeding season there are young and mates to be fed, so meals must be transported. This is a hazardous task because there are robbers lying in wait.

Arctic jaeger
Sterna parasiticus

HUNTERS, PIRATES, AND DIVERS. The Arctic jaeger can kill prey many times heavier than itself. The magnificent frigate bird steals food from other birds. It is shown here with its throat pouch inflated—part of a courtship ritual. The common, or great, cormorant, dives for its food. It is shown in characteristic pose—not drying its wings, but sunbathing to warm its stomach and speed up digestion.

Jaegers, known in Europe as skuas, are expert hunters. (The name jaeger is German for hunter.) They resemble gulls and are believed to have evolved from them, but there are important differences. The bill of a jaeger has a curved tip, and it is very strong. It can tear flesh. The feet are webbed, like those of other aquatic birds, but they also have sharp claws for seizing and gripping prey.

They are handsome birds, and strong, skillful fliers. They will attack and kill birds much bigger than themselves. They will also attack birds carrying food, harassing them until they drop it, then seizing it for themselves. If the victim resists, a jaeger may kill it. They also prowl around the edges of breeding colonies. Jaegers will grab eggs from any unattended nest and carry off chicks.

The long-tailed jaeger (*Stercorarius longicaudus*), of the Arctic, is recognizable by its extremely long central tail feathers. In summer it will eat berries, insects, eggs, and small birds. It also hunts lemmings. It lives by piracy in winter, when food is scarce.

Outside the breeding season they travel the world in search of food. One that was ringed as a chick in Antarctica was found five months later in Greenland. Another chick, ringed in Shetland, north of Scotland, was rescued from a German freeway and was shot soon afterward trying to steal a chicken on an Austrian farm.

Frigate Birds—Expert Pirates

Frigate birds (man-of-war birds) are named after frigates—small, fast warships—and they have a reputation for stealing. They steal food and nesting material from other birds, and in a spectacular fashion. The frigate bird chases its quarry until the food or other item is dropped, then catches it in mid-air. Frigate birds also catch their own food, however, scooping jellyfish, squid, and fish from the surface of tropical and subtropical seas. But they rarely alight on the water, and their feathers are not waterproof. Despite this disadvantage, they travel far from land, and the five species nest on remote islands.

They are large birds; the largest, the magnificent frigate bird (*Fregata magnificens*),

A COLONY OF BREEDING GANNETS *(opposite)*. All gannet colonies are this crowded and despite the fact that each bird can touch its neighbors all around it, the birds occupy territories and defend them. Experiments have found gannets fail to breed unless they are packed together in this way. These are African (or Cape) gannets *(Morus capensis)*.

has a wing span of up to 8 feet (2.45 m). But their most colorful feature is the red throat pouch the male inflates to impress females as part of a courtship ritual.

They breed on small, often remote islands. Male frigate birds gather on the ground in groups of up to 30. As the females fly overhead, the males inflate their throat pouches, throw back their heads to expose them, and vibrate their wings while calling to attract attention. When a female has made her choice, she lands beside the male, and the two perform a ritual involving much waving of their sinuous necks. They nest in trees if there are any, otherwise on the ground. The male collects nesting material, and the female builds the nest.

Gannets, Boobies, and Tropic Birds

Many birds can swim well enough to catch fish, but this requires the hunter to pursue its prey. It means the bird must be able to out-swim a fish. This is not easy, but there is an alternative: the fish can be taken by surprise from above.

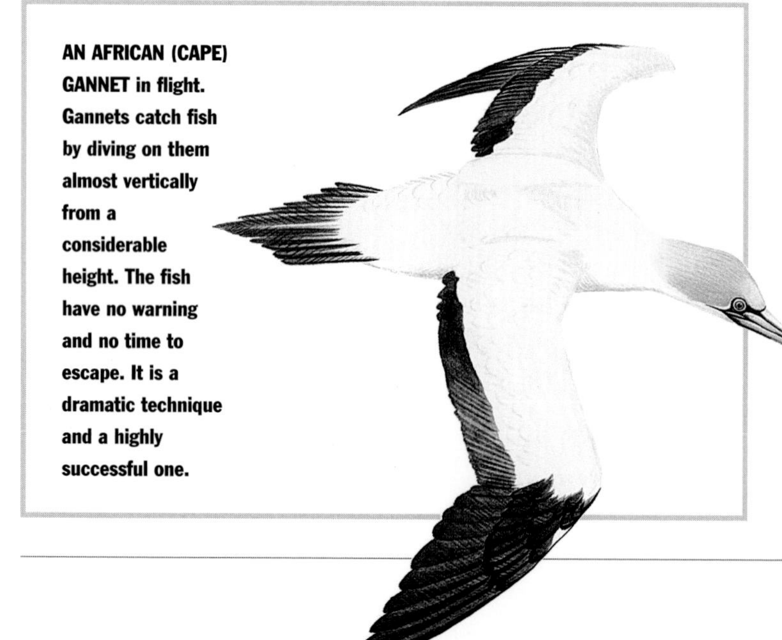

AN AFRICAN (CAPE) GANNET in flight. Gannets catch fish by diving on them almost vertically from a considerable height. The fish have no warning and no time to escape. It is a dramatic technique and a highly successful one.

The most impressive diving attackers are the gannets and boobies, members of the family Sulidae. Three species of gannets live in temperate regions, six species of boobies in the tropics and subtropics, but otherwise the two groups are very similar.

A gannet has a strong, stout body that tapers toward the head and tail, short legs, long, pointed wings, and a long bill with a sharp point and serrations along the edges. The bird's other adaptations to its hunting technique are less obvious. Its skull contains air sacs that absorb the shock of hitting the water and its nostrils are covered with a bony flap, so water cannot be forced into them. The bird breathes through gaps in the sides of its upper bill.

Gannets have a means of ridding their bodies of excess salt, allowing them to drink sea water and eat salty fish. Above each eye there are salt glands that secrete a very salty solution through the internal nostrils and into the bill, from where it drips away.

When a patrolling gannet sees a fish near the surface of the sea, it launches its attack. Folding back its wings to give it stability, the bird dives almost vertically from about 100 feet (30 m) into the water.

Boobies dive in the same way, but they have another specialty. They are very skilled at catching flying fish. They earned the name boobies because of their fearlessness. This meant they did not flee from sailors putting ashore for supplies, and many of them were killed.

Tropic birds also dive for fish, crustaceans, and squid, and, like boobies, they are skilled at catching flying fish. Although they dive at a steep

angle, they do not remain under water for long. There are three species of tropic birds, all belonging to the genus *Phaethon* and comprising the family Phaethontidae. As their name suggests, they live in the oceans of the tropics and subtropics. They are striking birds with white plumage bearing black markings and white or dark red central feathers on the tail that are as long as the rest of the bird. They used to be hunted for these feathers.

Tropic birds spend most of their lives alone and far out at sea, coming to land only during the breeding season. Then they form large and noisy colonies on cliffs.

Boobies breed on cliffs, or sometimes on beaches and even coral reefs. Gannets prefer rocks and islands. There they gather in thousands, and owing to the limited space that is available, the overcrowding is considerable. Each nesting bird can touch its neighbors all around. Despite this, each nest occupies a territory, and the birds defend their territories.

Crowding on this scale enhances security. It is very difficult for a predator to approach unnoticed or to decide where to attack. It also seems to be necessary for breeding. Attempts to raise small numbers of gannets have failed because the birds refused, or were unable, to breed. They appear to need the stimulus, one effect of which is to synchronize breeding, so all the eggs are laid and young raised during the same short period.

Pelicans

The brown pelican (*Pelecanus occidentalis*) dives for fish just like a gannet. Pelicans, gannets, and boobies all belong to the same order (Pelecaniformes), and they share some features. Unlike gannets and boobies, however, pelicans are famous for carrying food in a huge pouch below the lower bill. The pouch, called a gular pouch, extends from the throat. Although it is used to carry fish back to the nest during the breeding season, the pouch is not so much a basket for carrying food as a net for catching it.

There are eight species of pelicans, and only one of them dives. The others swim on the surface, dipping their bills in the water. Some species fish as a team, herding a shoal of fish into a space and then all feeding together.

As a bird fills its pouch with water and fish, the pouch stretches. The bird then closes its bill, pushing out the water but retaining the fish, which it swallows. Pelicans are strong fliers, and a loaded pouch would unbalance them by shifting the center of gravity, so they carry food for only short distances. They can travel long distances. In April 1998 a pelican from southern Europe flew about 1,200 miles (1,930 km) to the Norwegian town of Trysil, causing great excitement.

Pelicans are gregarious. They like crowds, and white pelicans usually nest on the ground in large numbers, like gannets. The nesting site is a noisy place once the eggs have hatched because young pelicans are highly vocal. Adults rarely make a sound. Brown, spot-billed, and pink-backed pelicans, on the other hand, usually nest in trees—still in large crowds.

American white pelican
Pelecanus erythrorhynchos

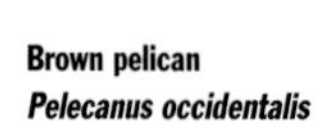

Brown pelican
Pelecanus occidentalis

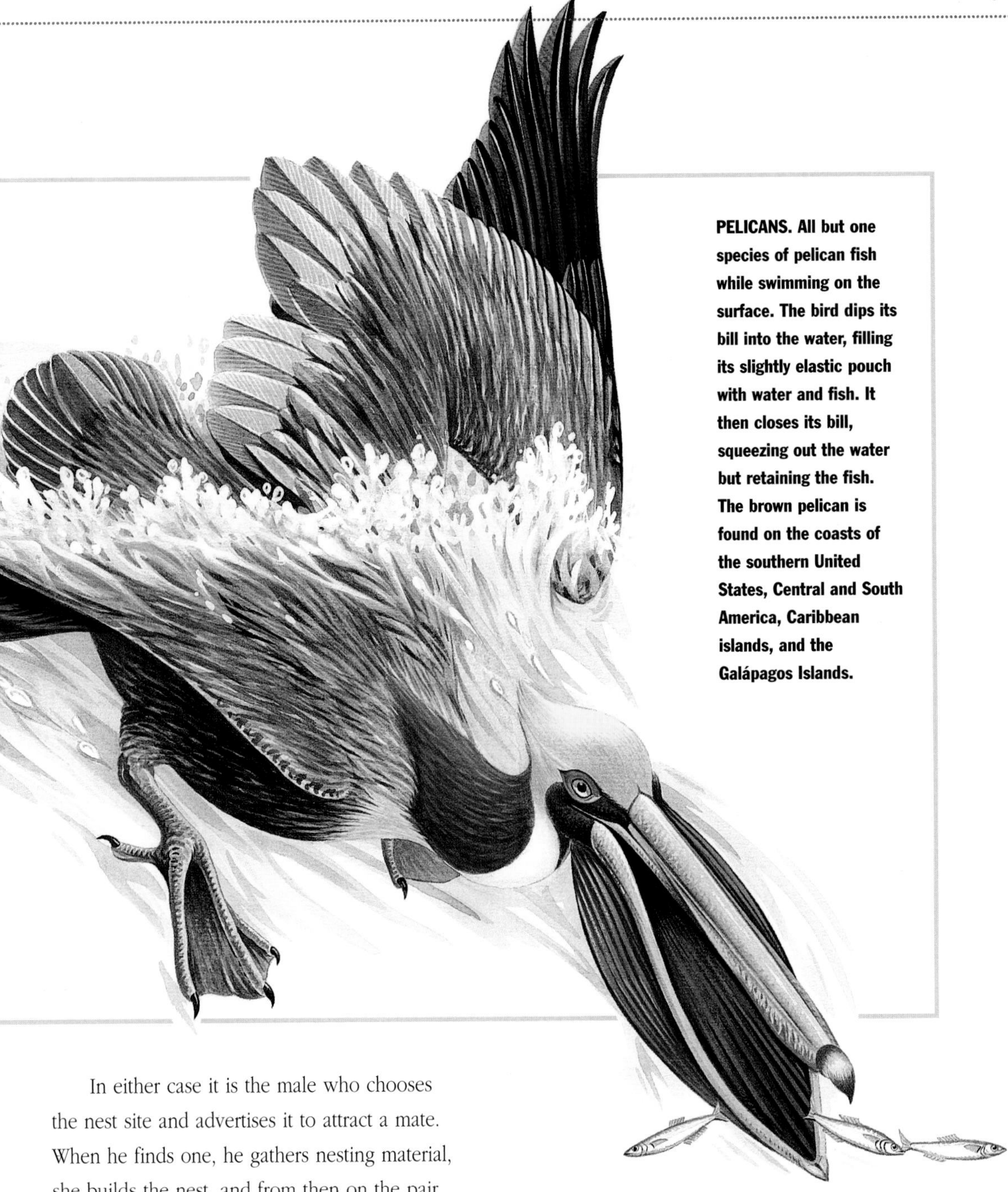

PELICANS. All but one species of pelican fish while swimming on the surface. The bird dips its bill into the water, filling its slightly elastic pouch with water and fish. It then closes its bill, squeezing out the water but retaining the fish. The brown pelican is found on the coasts of the southern United States, Central and South America, Caribbean islands, and the Galápagos Islands.

In either case it is the male who chooses the nest site and advertises it to attract a mate. When he finds one, he gathers nesting material, she builds the nest, and from then on the pair collaborate in incubating the eggs and caring for the chicks.

Raising pelican chicks is a demanding activity. They grow rapidly, which means they have very healthy appetites, and both parents must work to keep them satisfied. The chicks are fed with whole fish.

It is unusual for a pair of pelicans to raise more than one chick at a time. They may lay more than one egg, but they lay them several days apart and begin incubation as soon as the first one has been laid. The first chick to hatch will be ahead of the others and able to take more food from its parents.

Islands

In Lower Largo, a small village in eastern Scotland, there is a statue of Alexander Selkirk, a local man who left home to become a sailor. Having quarreled with his captain, he was put ashore in 1704 at his own request on the uninhabited island of Juan Fernández off the coast of Chile. He lived there until he was rescued in 1709. Later he became famous as the hero of a story by Daniel Defoe, who renamed him Robinson Crusoe.

There is a romance about islands. Perhaps it is because many—but by no means all—are remote places, where we imagine we might be far away from the stresses of everyday life. Perhaps we like to think we could make a new life for ourselves on a deserted island, like Robinson Crusoe, the Swiss Family Robinson, or some other marooned travelers. Some people have done just that. The inhabitants of Pitcairn Island, for example, are all descended from the mutineers of HMS *Bounty*.

First, though, it might be best to decide which kind of island to seek. Islands are not all the same. Some are near continents, others thousands of miles from the nearest land. Some are no more than barren rocks, many lack fresh water, and most of the habitable islands are already occupied.

As the last ice age drew to a close about 10,000 years ago, the ice sheets retreated. Meltwaters filled rivers, the rivers ran to the sea, and the sea level began to rise. The sea flooded the low-lying ground, but hilltops and other high ground remained above the water. Some hills were cut off. They became islands.

Islands farther from the coast may also be part of the nearest continent. Continents do not end abruptly at the coast—they shelve into the sea. An island up to about 200 miles (320 km) from a continent is likely to have risen from its shelf.

Other islands are much more distant and are not part of any continental shelf. They are, or were, volcanoes.

VOLCANIC ISLANDS

In 1963 a volcano erupted beneath the sea to the south of Iceland. It was a spectacular sight, shown live on television. Little by little, molten rock pouring from the volcanic vent cooled, solidified, and built a large mountain. After a time the top of the mountain emerged above the surface, black, smoking and steaming, and still growing higher. Then the eruption ended, leaving the world with a new island, Surtsey. In the years that followed, birds, insects, and plants colonized the new island.

Surtsey formed above the Mid-Atlantic Ridge, the line where two tectonic plates are moving apart and new rock is filling the gap. Iceland, its neighbor, is also a volcanic island, and its volcanoes are still active. Volcanoes are common near plate boundaries. On land a volcano can build a mountain. It can do the same if it erupts on the sea floor, and a big enough eruption in a shallow enough sea can produce an island.

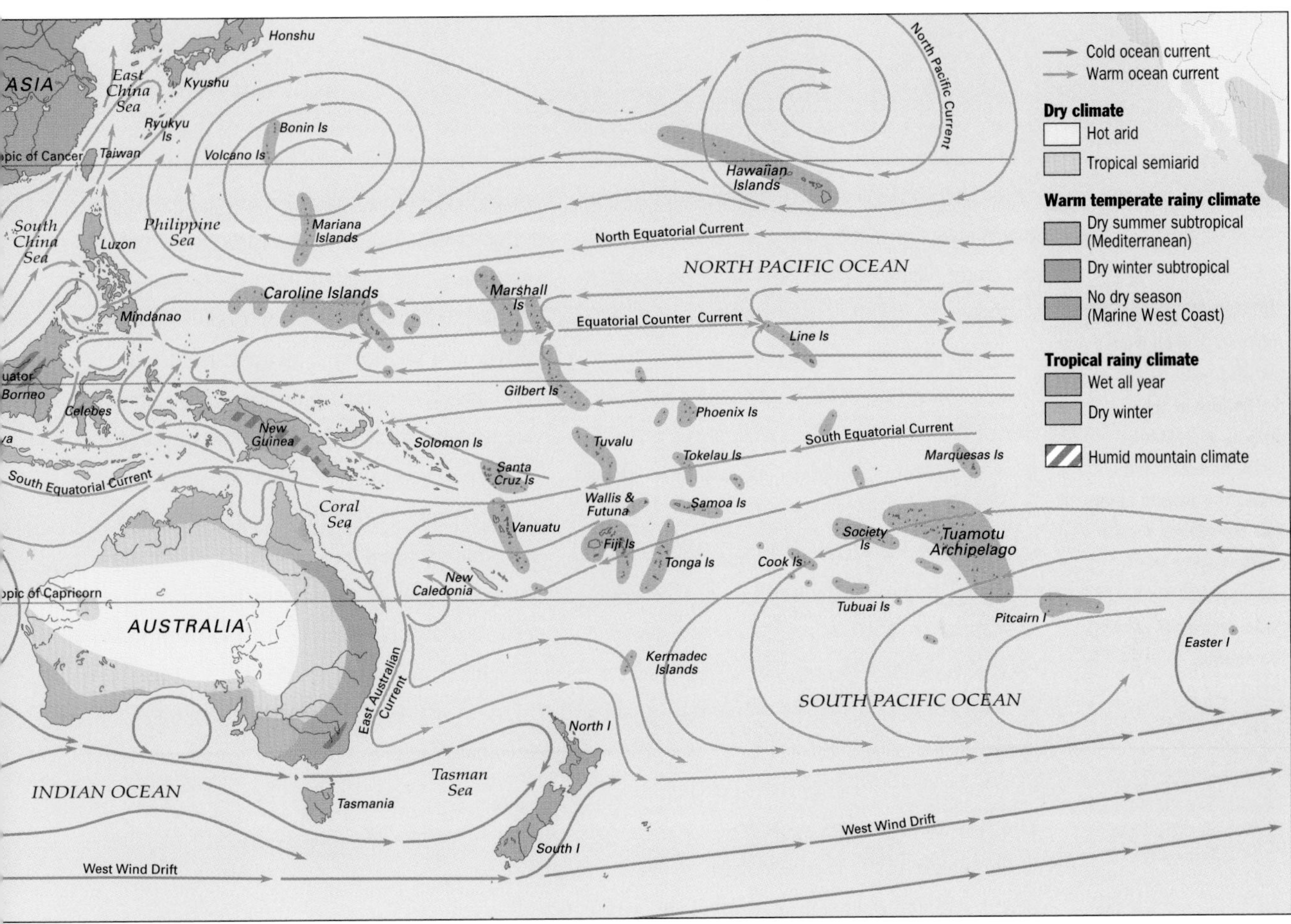

ISLANDS OF THE PACIFIC OCEAN. The map names the island groups and the better known individual islands, but there are many more small islands. As well as the location of the islands, the map shows the types of climates they experience and the ocean currents washing their shores.

Hot Spots

The composition of the Earth's crust varies from place to place. One result of this is that in some places there are pockets of molten rock—magma—in the mantle, beneath the crust. Rock within these pockets rises and cools by convection, but at the top, in the crust, the magma collects in a chamber, rises through a chimney it melts in the overlying rock, and erupts at the surface as a volcano.

Volcanic islands often form over these so-called hot spots. The hot spots are in the mantle, however, and the crustal rocks form plates that move above the mantle (see page 8). As the plate moves, the island moves with it, but the hot spot remains in the same place. The island moves, and later another island forms over the same hot spot. This process is sometimes repeated over and over, producing a chain or arc of islands.

Coral Islands and Atolls

It does not always happen in this way. Sometimes the submarine volcano does not reach the surface. A coral reef then forms on top of it, not far beneath the sea surface. A fall in sea level will then expose the reef as a coral island.

A reef can form around the rim of a volcanic crater. At first the crater may rise above the surface of the ocean, but over the years wind and rain will erode it. Then, when it is low enough, sea waves will break against it, eroding

THE HAWAIIAN ISLANDS *(opposite)*, seen from a satellite, with Hawaii at the bottom of the picture, then Maui, Lanai, Molokai, and Oahu. The picture shows how the islands form a chain, tracing the movement of the Pacific Plate over a hot spot in the mantle.

it even faster. While this is happening, the base of the volcano sinks slowly into the roof of the empty magma chamber beneath it. Eventually, the crater fills with water, and its rim reaches sea level.

Corals establish themselves on the volcanic rock, forming one or more reefs that follow the line of the crater rim. Then a slight fall in sea level or a rise in the underlying rock will expose the top of the reefs. There is then a circular coral island, or several islands forming a circle, enclosing an area of sheltered water. The island or islands are called an atoll, and the water they enclose is called a lagoon. The lagoon is only as deep as the crater it fills—some lagoons are fairly shallow.

The Hawaiian-Emperor Chain

In the middle of the Pacific Plate, far from any plate boundary, there is a mantle hot spot. At one time, about 70 million years ago, it was directly beneath a point off the Kamchatka Peninsula in eastern Russia. There is no island marking the spot, but there is an extinct volcano on the ocean floor called the Meiji Seamount.

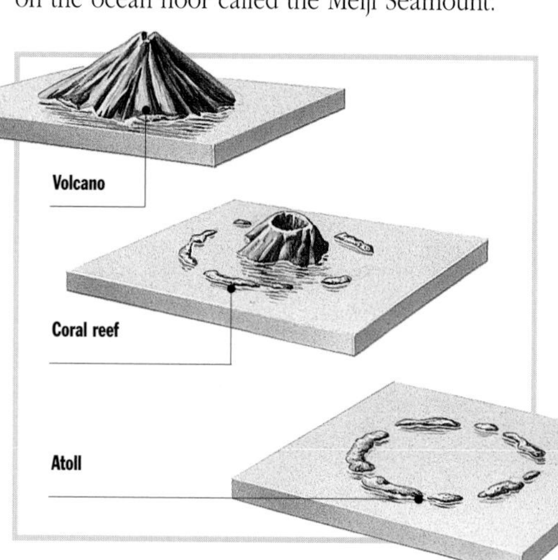

ATOLL FORMATION. An atoll is a circular coral reef enclosing a lagoon. It forms as a volcano subsides beneath the ocean. Coral colonizes the rim of the crater. As it sinks further, the coral reef builds higher. A lowering of the sea level then exposes the reef.

The plate continued to move northward, and more volcanoes formed. These are now a chain of seamounts called the Emperor Seamounts, extending from south of Kamchatka to a point about level with San Francisco, which was the position of the hot spot 50 million years ago.

About 40 million years ago it reached what are now the Midway Islands, two islands enclosed inside an atoll. Then the plate changed direction and started moving northwest. More volcanoes formed, this time rising above the surface as islands, the Hawaiian chain. The present Hawaiian islands began to emerge about 10 million years ago, and the hot spot has been in its present location beneath Hawaii itself for less than 2 million years.

CORAL REEFS

A coral reef is a colony of polyps, small animals belonging to the class Anthozoa, the "flower-animals." A polyp is very like a sea anemone, the difference being that the polyp secretes a protective coat of calcium carbonate, so it lives inside its own cup, called a corallite, extending its tentacles through the open upper end to capture food.

Polyps reproduce by budding off new individuals, which settle down nearby and make their own corallites. Adjacent corallites fuse, so the reef is a huge mass of calcium carbonate, all of it produced by coral polyps. Over thousands of years the skeletons of dead corals add to the coral reef.

There are two types of corals: hermatypic and ahermatypic. Ahermatypic

corals live in all the oceans, but it is only hermatypic corals that form reefs, and they live only in warm seas.

Coral polyps are carnivores. They cannot move to catch their prey, so they rely on the movement of the water. Their tentacles subdue prey—microscopic animals—by stinging it. They are helped, however, by single-celled organisms called zooxanthellae. These live inside the tissues of the polyps and produce carbohydrates by photosynthesis. In ways scientists do not fully understand, the zooxanthellae feed the polyps.

The combined needs of the zooxanthellae and polyps determine where reefs can form. Because the zooxanthellae need light for photosynthesis, they are restricted to fairly clear water and depths, depending on the clarity of the water, of 33–200 feet (10–60 m). The polyps need warmth. They cannot survive in water with a surface temperature below 68°F (20°C). Nor can they survive where the salinity (salt content) of the water is outside the ordinary range for sea water, between 32‰ and 35‰ (‰ means parts per thousand, or "per mill"). The overall result is that coral reefs form only in shallow seas between latitudes 30°N and 30°S.

Reef Communities

Coral reefs grow in the marine equivalent of deserts; the clear blue water around them contains very few living organisms or plant nutrients. Despite this, they are among the most diverse and productive communities of organisms on Earth. They are believed to achieve this by refusing to part with any nutrient that comes within their reach, recycling everything with extraordinary efficiency.

Algae settle on the surface of the coral, and they, along with the zooxanthellae, perform photosynthesis. These provide the base of a complex food web. Some of the planktonic organisms rise to feed near the sea surface at night, settling on the reef by day and bringing food down with them.

Components of the ecosystem

1 Phytoplankton
2 Algae
3 Detritus
4 Zooplankton
5 Fanworm
6 Coral shrimp
7 Damselfish
8 Clam
9 Brittlestar
10 Reef crab
11 Corals
12 Barracuda
13 Sea urchin
14 Sea slug
15 Starfish
16 Butterfly fish
17 Octopus

Energy flow

Primary producer /primary consumer
Primary/secondary consumer
Secondary/tertiary consumer
Dead material /consumer
Death

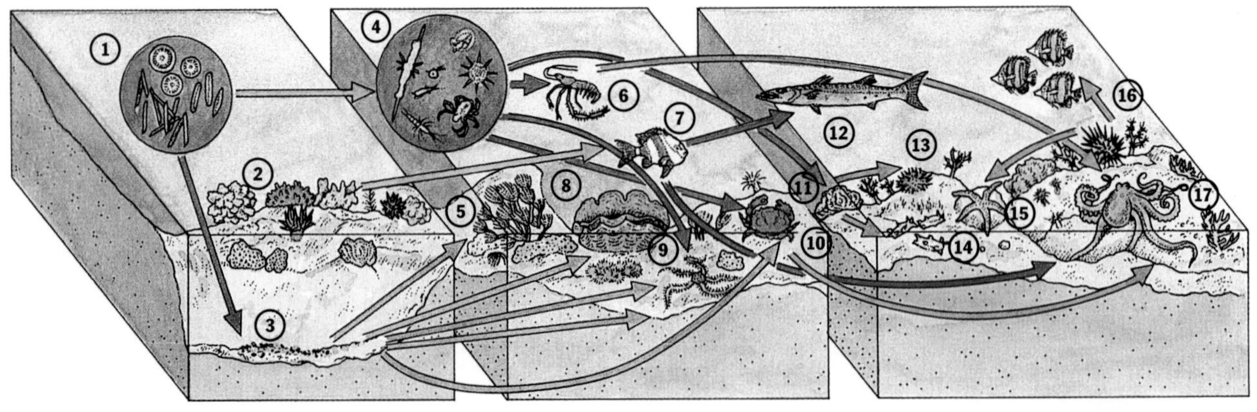

A CORAL REEF ECOSYSTEM. The system is based on planktonic plants and animals, which support the intricate and colorful corals, made by polyps, and other invertebrates. The crevices of the reef shelter many of the fish that graze around the corals, as well as their larger predators such as barracudas.

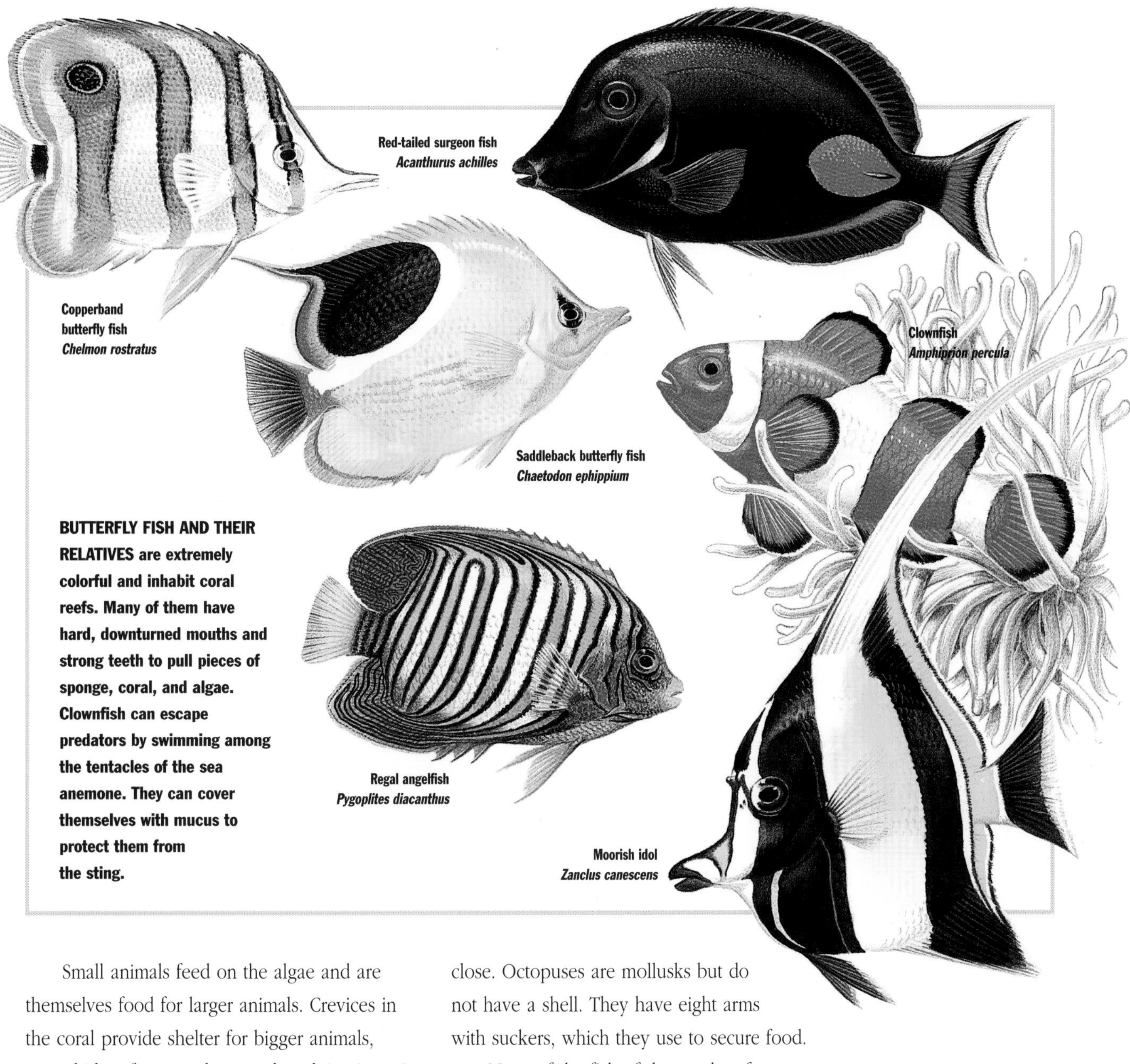

BUTTERFLY FISH AND THEIR RELATIVES are extremely colorful and inhabit coral reefs. Many of them have hard, downturned mouths and strong teeth to pull pieces of sponge, coral, and algae. Clownfish can escape predators by swimming among the tentacles of the sea anemone. They can cover themselves with mucus to protect them from the sting.

Small animals feed on the algae and are themselves food for larger animals. Crevices in the coral provide shelter for bigger animals, some hiding from predators, others lying in wait for prey. Sea anemones and sponges live on the surface of the coral. The sea horse (family Syngnathidae) also lives there.

The reef is also inhabited by sea cucumbers (related to starfish and sea urchins) and sea slugs. Octopuses and eels lurk in dark corners, ready to snatch any unwary fish that come too close. Octopuses are mollusks but do not have a shell. They have eight arms with suckers, which they use to secure food.

Many of the fish of the coral reef are brightly colored. The mandarin fish, for example, gets its name from its resemblance to the brightly colored silk clothing worn by mandarins (top-ranking officials) in China. Patterns of stripes and patches act as camouflage, breaking up the outline of the fish and making it difficult to see, while bright colors often help them attract mates.

SILVERSWORD *(Argyroxiphium sandwichense)* growing at a high altitude on the edge of a volcanic crater in Hawaii, where it withstands heat and snow. It is endemic to Hawaii (only found there).

ISOLATION AND EVOLUTION

Islands are isolated. The open sea presents a formidable barrier to plants and animals. It can be crossed, but not easily. Seeds can be carried by the wind, on ocean currents, or by birds that have been accidentally blown out to sea. Flying insects and small spiders ballooning on their long threads can also travel long distances by air. Lizards, snakes, and small rodents escaping from a flood by clinging to fallen vegetation can be carried out to sea and washed up on an island shore. Species can move along an archipelago by "island hopping" in this way, but it is a haphazard affair.

Once they arrive, species occupy the available space and soon take over the resources, making it more difficult for later arrivals to establish themselves. The islanders are now isolated from other members of their own species on the mainland. They can no longer interbreed with them. Evolution—the changes that take place in organisms over successive generations—is a gradual process, but on islands it can be accelerated as plants and animals adapt to local conditions. This is called adaptive radiation, and it leads to the emergence of new species.

ENDEMIC PLANTS

Species that are found in only one area of the world are called endemics. Many very remote islands are rich in endemics.

Silverswords, for example, are four species of woody plants found in the Hawaiian islands. They belong to their own genus, *Argyroxiphium*, and there is nowhere else in the world where they grow naturally. Ninety percent of all the native Hawaiian plants are endemic. Three-quarters of the plants native to New Zealand are endemic, and the proportion of endemic plants in Saint Helena is 85 percent. Saint Helena is one of the most remote islands, situated 1,150 miles (1,850 km) away from the coast of Africa. It is very small—only 47 square miles (122 sq. km) in area.

For an island to be rich in endemics, it must be far from land and in a low latitude. Offshore islands have few endemic species because the sea barrier is not wide enough. In Britain, for example, fewer than 1 percent of the plants are endemic. Most British plants also occur in continental Europe. Iceland is more isolated, but it also has few endemics. The reason for this is the relatively short time that has elapsed since the island lay beneath an ice sheet. As a result there has not been time for endemics to evolve.

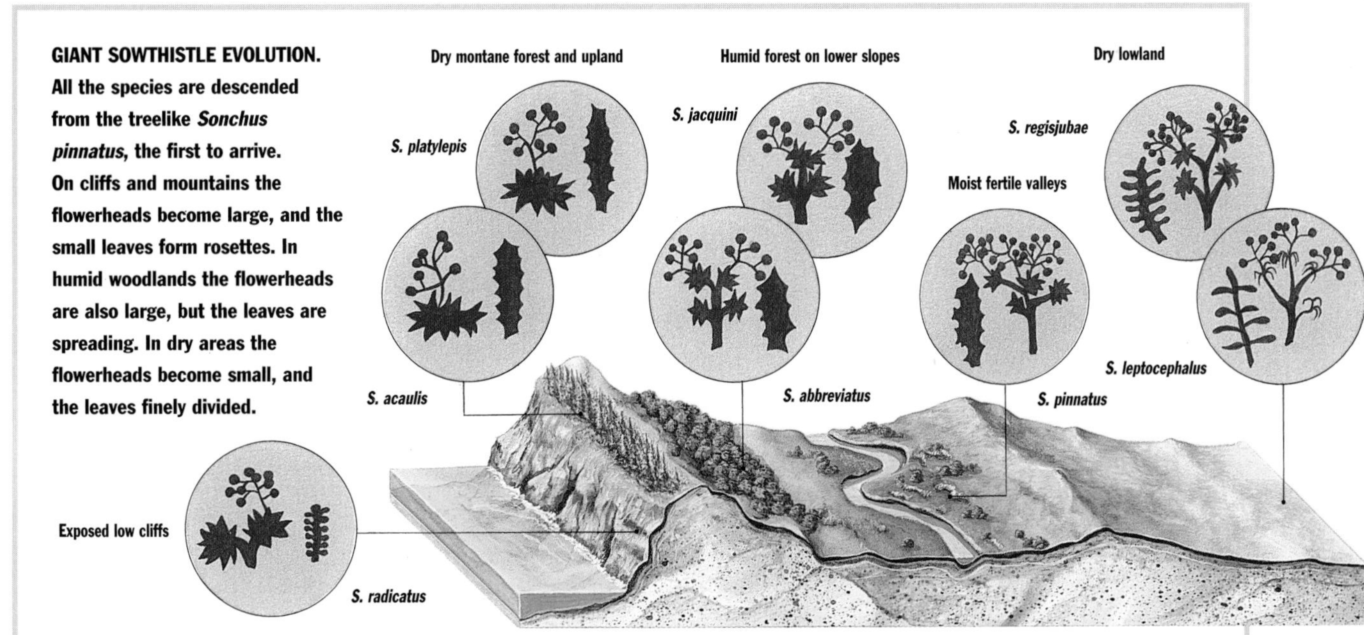

GIANT SOWTHISTLE EVOLUTION. All the species are descended from the treelike *Sonchus pinnatus*, the first to arrive. On cliffs and mountains the flowerheads become large, and the small leaves form rosettes. In humid woodlands the flowerheads are also large, but the leaves are spreading. In dry areas the flowerheads become small, and the leaves finely divided.

Endemics on the Canary Islands

The Canary Islands form an archipelago of 13 islands with a combined area of 2,808 square miles (7,273 sq. km) in the Atlantic Ocean. At the nearest point the distance to the African coast is 67 miles (108 km).

Just over one-third of the plants—more than 300 species—found in the Canary Islands are endemic, and have relatives on the mainland. Some came from the Mediterranean region, and others from East Africa. They were carried in the digestive tracts of birds, attached to their plumage or carried by winds or ocean currents, and they have adapted to their local habitats.

In drier parts of the islands there are 25 species of the genus *Euphorbia*, plants resembling cacti that arrived from Africa. The houseleeks (*Sempervivum* species) and the dragon tree (*Dracaena draco*) also arrived from Africa. In the mountains *Echium wildpretii*, a member of the bugloss family (Boraginaceae), produces a rosette of silvery leaves and tall spikes of flowers. This plant has relatives throughout the warmer parts of Europe, but it is one of several that occur only in the Canaries. *Canarina canariensis*, the Canary bellflower, is one of three species in the genus. The other two are native to tropical East Africa.

ENDEMIC ANIMALS

Animals also settle on remote islands and evolve into new species. A flock of small finches, or honeycreepers, flew, or was blown, more than 1,860 miles (3,000 km) across the Pacific and came to rest on Hawaii. There they survived, reproduced, and their descendants migrated to the other islands.

The first birds are thought to have resembled what is now called the Nihoa finch (*Telespyza ultima*). Since their arrival and expansion they have evolved into 28 variously colored species in 15 genera. There are finches that feed on insects, nectar, fruit, snails, seeds, and the eggs of sea birds, and they have bills shaped to their particular diets.

Another group of finches lives on the Galápagos Islands in the Pacific, about 650 miles (1,046 km) from the west coast of Ecuador. Charles Darwin (1809–1882) visited the islands in 1835, and collected specimens. Studies of these helped him develop his theory of evolution by natural selection—the survival of those organisms that are best adapted to the environmental conditions.

Of the 26 species of land birds on the islands, 21 were endemic. These included 14 species of finches, all descended from a mainland common ancestor. Of these, 13 are endemic to the Galápagos, and one is also found 400 miles (644 km) away on Cocos Island.

Madagascar's Primates

Madagascar is a large island off the east coast of Africa. It is separated from the mainland by the Mozambique Channel, 248 miles (400 km) wide at its narrowest point. Fifty percent of all species of chameleons are found on Madagascar, but its most famous residents are primates.

Their ancestors were marooned on the island some 50 million years ago, and since then they have evolved in isolation. They now comprise four families, with a total of 12 genera

HAWAIIAN FINCHES. These are just a few of the 28 species, all of which are descended from a single common ancestor that reached the islands long ago. They have adapted to different feeding niches and differ mainly in their beak types. The iiwi, for example, has a bill shaped for reaching inside a flower and sipping nectar, while the Maui parrotbill uses its lower bill to chisel into branches and its upper bill to extract beetles and their grubs.

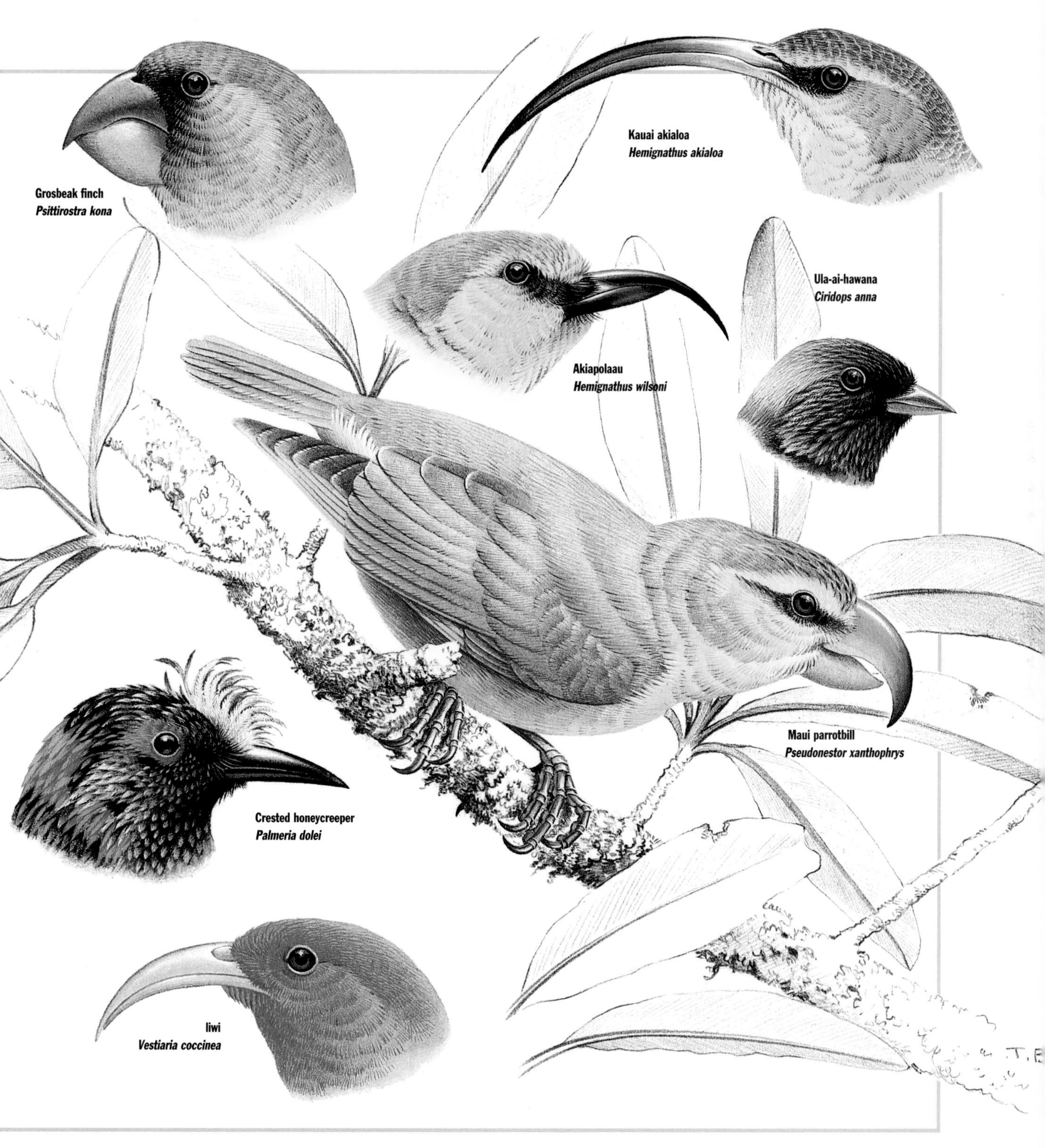
Grosbeak finch
Psittirostra kona
Kauai akialoa
Hemignathus akialoa
Ula-ai-hawana
Ciridops anna
Akiapolaau
Hemignathus wilsoni
Maui parrotbill
Pseudonestor xanthophrys
Crested honeycreeper
Palmeria dolei
Iiwi
Vestiaria coccinea

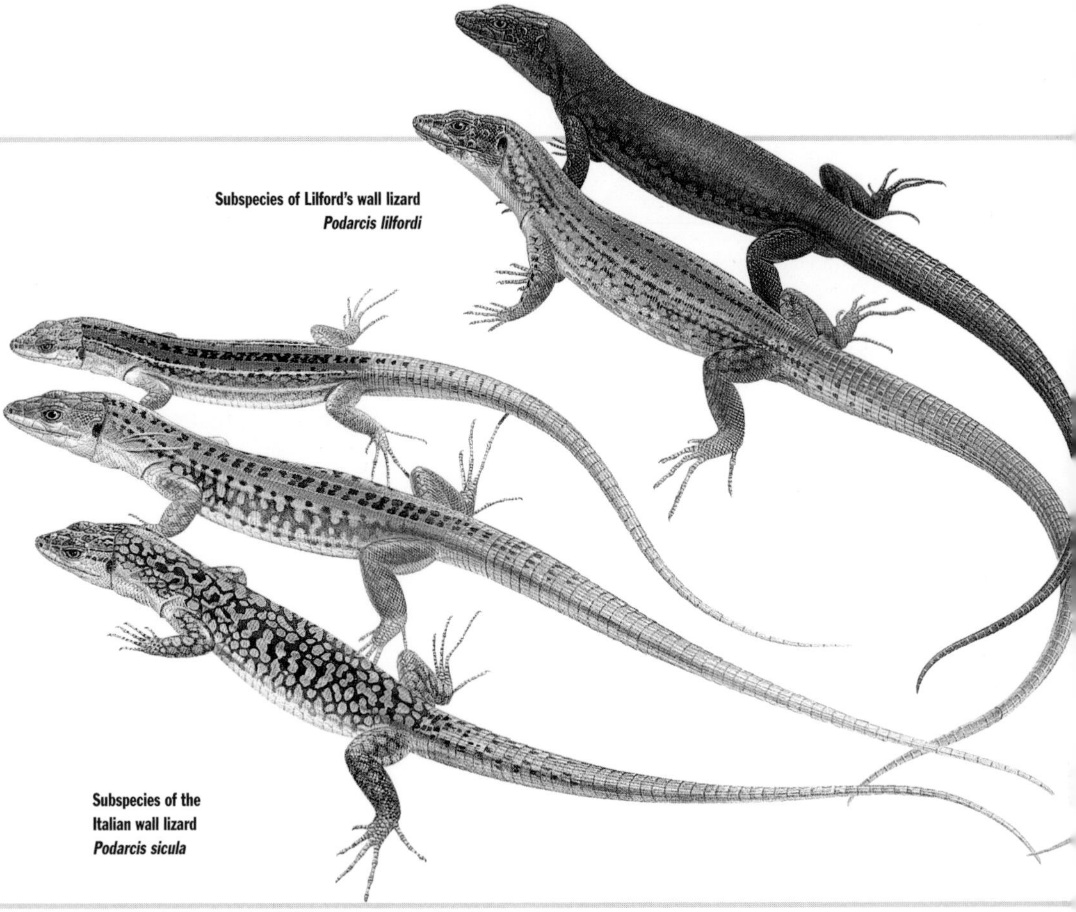

BALEARIC ISLAND LIZARDS. When the Balearic Islands became cut off from the mainland by the rising waters of the Mediterranean sea, populations evolved in isolation, producing many new species and subspecies. The Moroccan wall lizard was introduced to Minorca from northwest Africa in 1968.

Subspecies of Lilford's wall lizard
Podarcis lilfordi

Subspecies of the Italian wall lizard
Podarcis sicula

and 22 species, all of them endemic to Madagascar and the adjacent, smaller islands. There were several more species in the past, but they are now extinct, and the species that inhabit the island today are all endangered to a greater or lesser degree.

Lemurs, of the family Lemuridae, form the most diverse group of primates on Madagascar. There are ten species of them, the largest about the size of a cat. They have rather doglike faces, large eyes, long bushy tails, and long hind limbs.

Lemurs live mainly in the trees, although some species often visit the ground, and the ring-tailed lemur (*Lemur catta*) spends much of its time there. The dwarf lemurs (family Cheirogaleidae) are much smaller, some only 4 inches (12.5 cm) long not counting the 6-inch (15-cm) tail. The indri (*Indri indri*) is about 2 feet (60 cm) long, with a 2-inch (5-cm) tail. With the woolly lemur (*Avahi laniger*) and two species of sifakas (genus *Propithecus*), it belongs to the family Indriidae. Finally, there is the aye-aye (*Daubentonia madagascariensis*), the only species in the family Daubentoniidae. It is nocturnal and feeds on fruit and insects, using its strong incisor teeth to cut through the shells of fruits—it can open a coconut with them—and its extremely long, thin, middle finger to extract the juice and flesh.

Tortoises and Lizards

Galápago is the Spanish word for "tortoise" and

it was Spanish sailors who gave the Galápagos Islands their name. During the 16th century Spanish ships used to call at the islands for supplies; the tortoises were popular as food.

The Galápagos giant tortoises have carapaces (shells) about 4 feet (1.2 m) long. They were once widespread on the mainland, but became extinct. Having arrived, the tortoises dispersed to six of the islands in the group. Then, isolated from each other, the six populations started to change the shapes of their carapaces until there were six types, and the shape of its carapace indicated the island from which a tortoise came. They are all the same species, *Geochelone elephantopus*, but the six types are classified as subspecies.

Iguana lizards also crossed to the Galápagos Islands, and some adapted so they could feed on cactus. Others learned to swim and took to the sea, living on a diet of seaweed scraped from the rocks. With an adaptation that allowed them to rid their bodies of excess salt, the marine iguanas (*Amblyrhynchus cristatus*) became the only sea-going lizards in the world.

Lizards of the Balearic Islands

The Balearic Islands, in the western Mediterranean, consist of Majorca, Minorca, Ibiza, Formentera, Cabrera, and 11 islets (small islands). They were originally hills that became islands when water came rushing through the Strait of Gibraltar at the end of the last ice age.

By that time several local species of wall and rock lizards were living there. Isolated by the rising sea level, they adapted to their surroundings. The wall lizards (*Podarcis* species) and the Moroccan rock lizard (*Lacerta perspicillata*) now exist as several subspecies, distinguishable by their colors and markings.

GIANT TORTOISE ADAPTATIONS. The carapaces of the giant tortoises of the Galápagos Islands have evolved into different shapes on different islands.

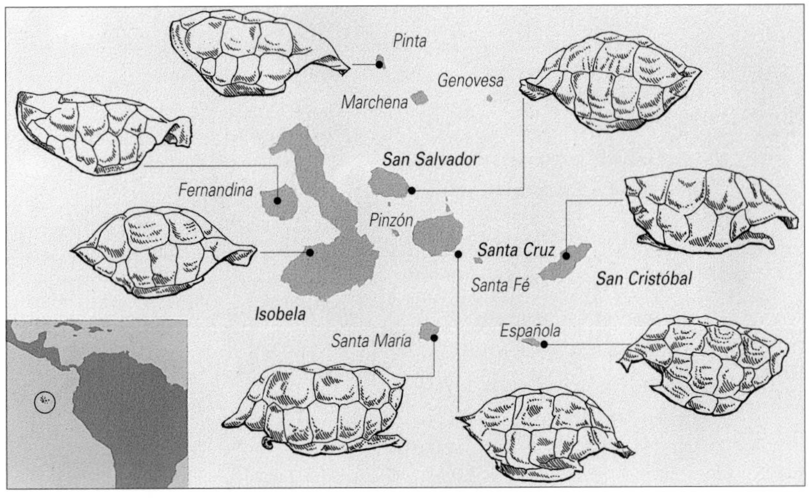

Survival of the Oceans

The oceans are so vast, covering so large an area with such an immense volume of water that it is difficult to imagine how anything could harm them. The waters of the oceans are unlikely to be harmed by anything we do. Smaller seas and coastal waters are vulnerable, however; they can be polluted. Some endemic species on remote islands are now in danger of becoming extinct.

EL NIÑO. Trade winds drive warm surface water to the west, allowing the cold Peru Current to rise to the surface off the South American coast. During an El Niño, the trade winds slacken and the pool of warm water deepens, suppressing the upwelling.

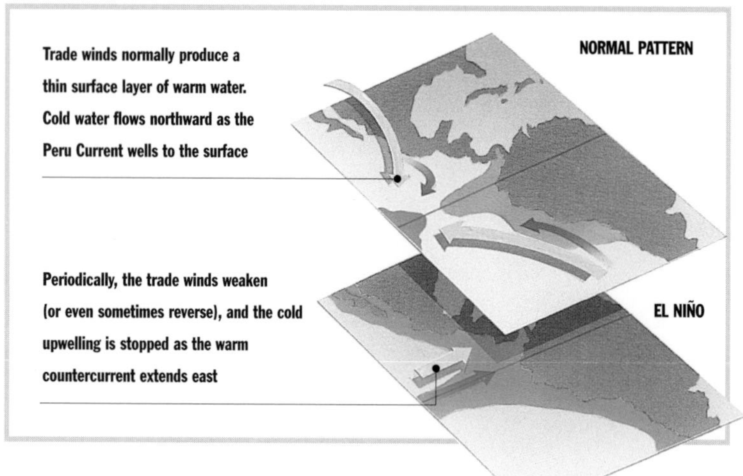

Many island endemics have become threatened with extinction. When people settle on islands, they bring plants and animals with them. Some are brought deliberately to provide food, fiber, and other useful materials. Others arrive hidden in cargoes or as seeds on people's boots. These are called tramp species. Once arrived, tramp species that become naturalized can thrive to supplant native species. Now, it is often illegal for people to harm endemics, but they are still at some risk.

Natural phenomena can also cause harm to life in and around the ocean. Off the west coast of South America the Peru, or Humboldt, Current flows north from the Southern Ocean, carrying cold water. As it approaches the equator, it reaches a region where the layer of warm surface water is very shallow. The cold water wells up to the surface, bringing with it plant nutrients carried all the way from Antarctica. These nutrients sustain a large population of plankton. Huge shoals of fish feed on the plankton.

The layer of warm water is cool because the prevailing winds, blowing from the east, drive the Equatorial Current that carries the warm water toward Indonesia. There it collects as a deep pool. Every few years, however, the pattern changes. The winds slacken or cease to blow. Warm surface water flows from west to east, accumulates off South America, and suppresses the upwelling cold water. The supply of nutrients fails, the plankton die, and the fish disappear. This change in the current happens around Christmas, and it is called El Niño, "the (boy) child." It also affects the weather over much of the world.

OVERFISHING

El Niño drives away the fish, but they come back. Persistently catching fish faster than breeding can replace them, however, does much more serious harm, and in the last few decades overfishing has become a concern.

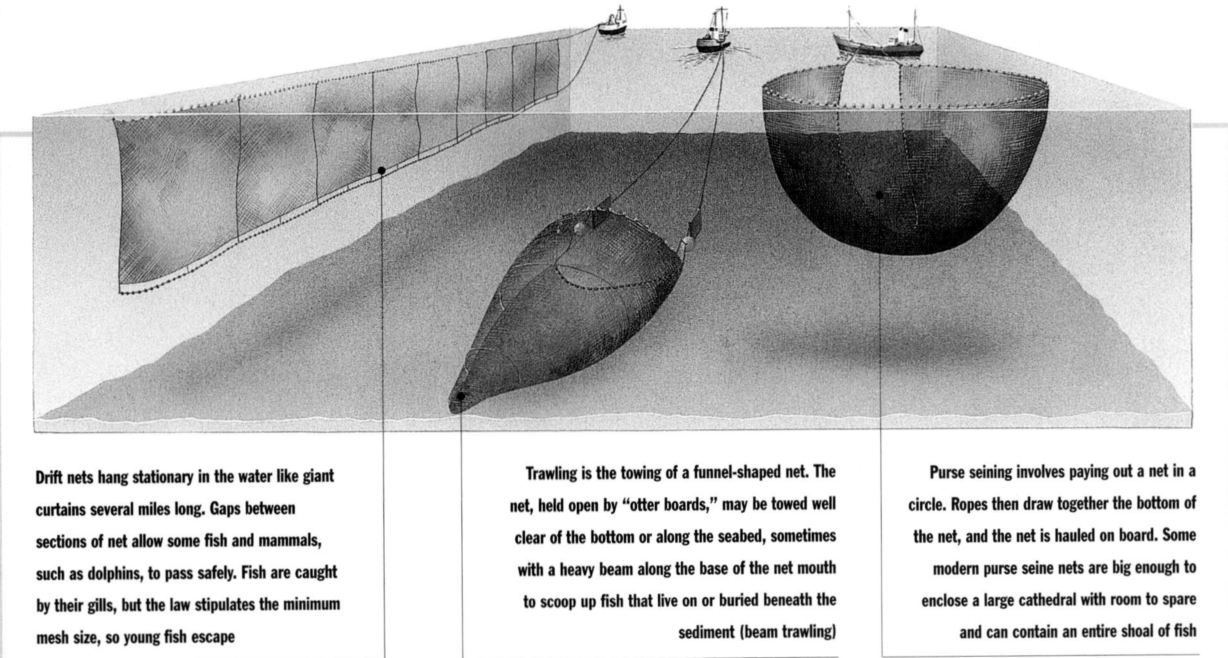

Drift nets hang stationary in the water like giant curtains several miles long. Gaps between sections of net allow some fish and mammals, such as dolphins, to pass safely. Fish are caught by their gills, but the law stipulates the minimum mesh size, so young fish escape

Trawling is the towing of a funnel-shaped net. The net, held open by "otter boards," may be towed well clear of the bottom or along the seabed, sometimes with a heavy beam along the base of the net mouth to scoop up fish that live on or buried beneath the sediment (beam trawling)

Purse seining involves paying out a net in a circle. Ropes then draw together the bottom of the net, and the net is hauled on board. Some modern purse seine nets are big enough to enclose a large cathedral with room to spare and can contain an entire shoal of fish

Modern fishing is very intensive. Fishing vessels carry instruments to locate fish, and their powerful engines make it possible for them to fish with very large nets. A purse seine net, for example, is paid out in a circle to surround an entire shoal. Ropes then draw together the bottom of the net, turning it into a bag. As the net is hauled on board, the shoal spills into the fish hold.

A fully equipped ship is very expensive to buy and to operate. With loans to repay, with interest, owners have no choice but to catch as many fish as possible. The consequence is that stocks of many important species have declined.

Conservation of fish stocks is based on calculations of the size of catches the population can sustain. These are based on estimates of the size of each stock, the rate at which the fish are reproducing, and how their rate of reproduction may change in future years. Catches are then restricted by various means. Quotas are often allocated for each species, so that only a resricted number are caught. Alternatively, boats may be forbidden to sail on a specified number of days each year. Reducing the size of the fishing fleet by paying owners to scrap boats is a more permanent way of limiting catches.

POLLUTION

Rivers carry water that has drained from the surrounding land. Dissolved in this water are plant nutrients washed from the soil and other soluble chemical compounds. The water may carry traces of pesticides: chemicals that are used to combat pests such as insects. As the river passes through towns, rainwater flows into it through storm drains. The rainwater has crossed roofs and roads before entering the drains, and it has gathered dust, oil, and other substances. In some countries industrial waste and sewage is

OCEAN FISHING. Commercial sea fishing operates on a big scale, using powerful ships, instruments to locate fish shoals, navigational aids, and huge nets. It is so expensive that owners cannot afford not to catch as many fish as possible. Many important fish stocks have been reduced, and there is a risk some of them may collapse. The fish will not become extinct, but fishing communities will suffer badly.

POLLUTION. A plastic bag has caught on this elkhorn coral near the Bahamas. By shutting out the light it will prevent photosynthesis, on which the coral depends.

still discharged into rivers without being treated.

The rivers flow into the sea, and their fresh water meets salt water. The two do not mix, but chemical reactions occur that cause small particles to cling together in lumps—the process is called flocculation—and the lumps settle to the bottom. This is the most serious cause of pollution at sea. It affects only coastal waters and is more severe in some seas than others. Seas that are almost enclosed by land suffer the worst. Often there are many rivers discharging into them, and pollutants tend to accumulate because the limited contact with the ocean means the water changes only slowly.

The United Nations Environment Program has secured agreements to reduce pollution among countries bordering most of the seas.

Some marine organisms are much more susceptible than others to pollution. Discharges into the sea often make the water cloudy or alter its salinity, and this can kill coral reefs, which need clear water and tolerate a fairly narrow range of temperature and salinity.

Oil

Oil is the best-known pollutant, mainly because accidental spills from tankers are widely reported. Accidents are not the principal cause of oil pollution, however. At one time much more oil was spilled from tankers. They cleaned their tanks at sea by pumping water into them and allowing the water to float the oil out into the sea. This practice is now illegal, but it used to cause severe pollution, especially in the Mediterranean, which was a convenient place to wash out the tanks for ships passing through the Suez Canal and the Mediterranean on their way between Europe and the Atlantic and the Persian Gulf oil terminals.

Oil also reaches the sea from rivers, and from the air. Smoke from factories and vehicles contains unburned fuel that is washed down by the rain. This pollution from land is a problem in coastal areas but has little effect over the open ocean.

WHALING

In the 1930–1931 Antarctic whaling season 25,000 blue whales were killed, amounting to 80 percent of the total whale catch. In the

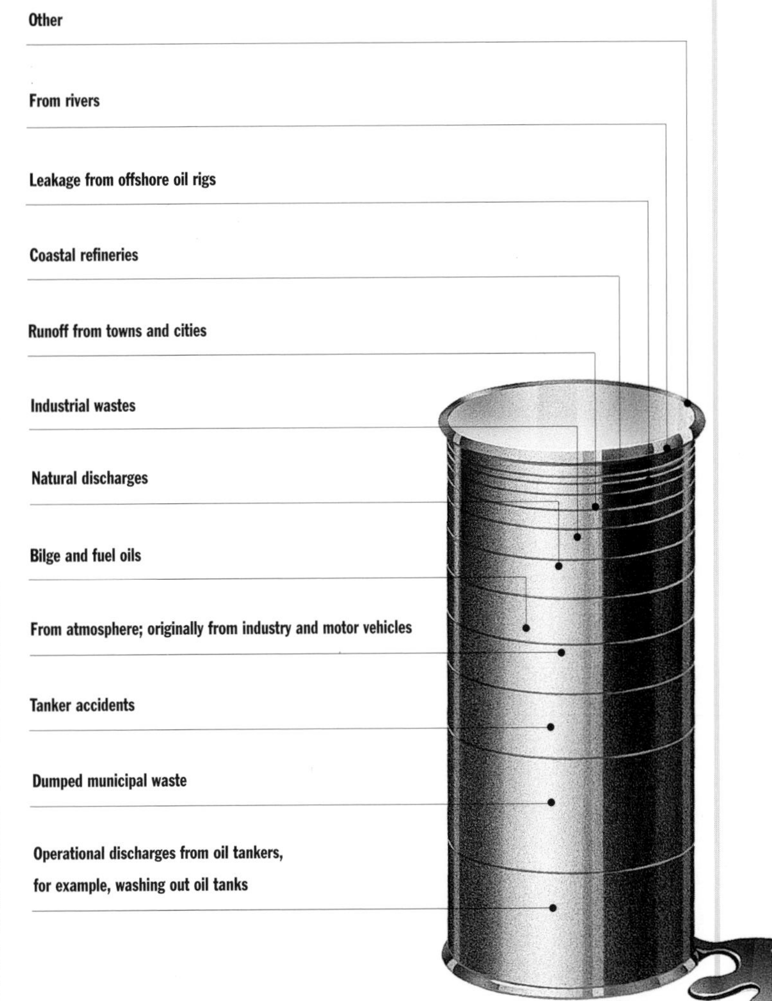

SOURCES OF OIL POLLUTION. Surprisingly, tanker accidents account for only one-eighth of marine oil pollution. By far the largest amounts are discharged by tankers during operations or are released from dumped municipal wastes.

AREAS OF MARINE POLLUTION. Pollution is a serious problem only in coastal waters and seas that are largely enclosed by land because the pollutants are discharged from the land, mainly through rivers. The map on the left below shows the location of persistent pollution of all kinds. The map on the right shows the location of oil slicks caused by the discharge of oil by tankers on the world's major shipping routes.

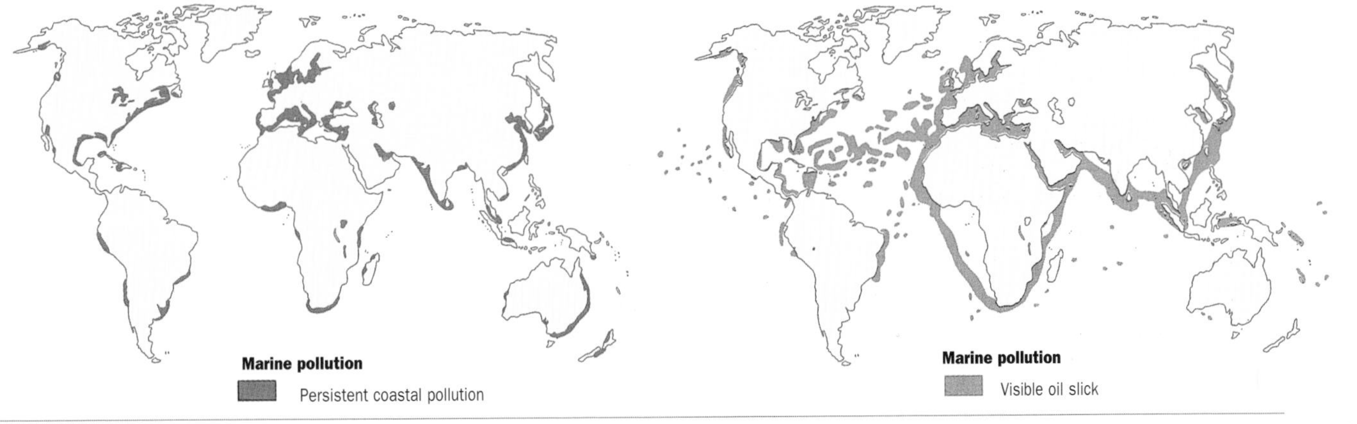

STOPPING THE KILLING *(opposite)*. Greenpeace, the international organization dedicated to preserving endangered species and campaigning against environmental abuses, has campaigned against whaling since it was founded in 1971. Nonviolent direct actions have included literally coming between the whalers' harpoon guns and their prey. Here, Greenpeace campaigns against a Japanese ship processing minke whales.

1963–1964 season only 112 were caught. A few years later blue whales were given complete protection, making it illegal to hunt them. Their numbers are recovering, but blue whales are still rare, and the species remains endangered.

This was not the first species to suffer. Early European whalers preferred the Greenland, or bowhead, right whale (*Balaena mysticetus*) or the Biscay, or black, right whale (*B. glacialis*). These were the "right" whales to hunt, hence the name. They were right because they are slow in the water, easy to kill, and their carcasses float—those of other baleen whales sink. It has been illegal to hunt Greenland right whales since the early 20th century and the Biscay right whale since 1929.

THE SPINNER DOLPHIN *(Stenella longirostris)* feeds on tuna and is often caught in fishing nets and drowned. To avoid this, various actions are taken. (1) The fishing boat launches inflatable craft to round up the fish (a) and the dolphins chasing them (b). (2) While the inflatables prevent the fish escaping, a purse seine net is lowered, enclosing both fish and dolphins. (3) The bottom of the net is pulled beneath the fish. (4) The net is drawn toward the boat. (5) Some dolphins escape by leaping over the edge of the net, and those that fail to do so are helped by hand, by fishermen in the inflatables or by divers.

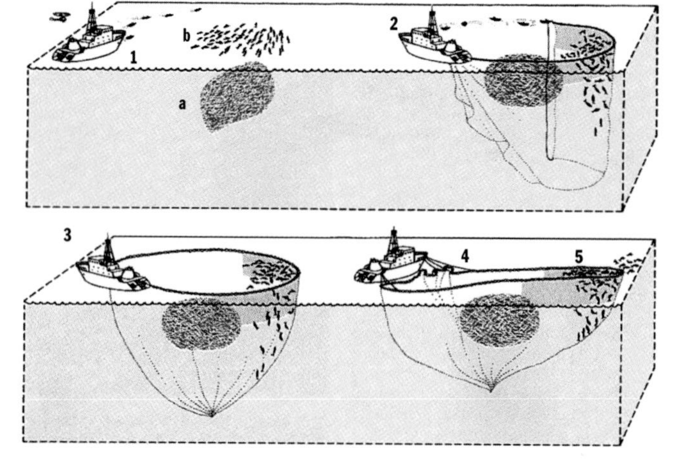

The decline in the blue whale population, due to killing the animals faster than they could breed, forced the whalers to hunt other species. Predictably, each of those species also became less numerous.

In 1986 a moratorium on all whaling for ten years was imposed. Although some whales continued to be killed, the moratorium allowed populations to recover to some extent, and minke whales have become fairly abundant. The story of whaling could be repeated with fishing, at least for some stocks, although it is unlikely that any species of fish could be brought close to extinction, as happened to some whale species.

Dolphins under Threat

It is not necessary to hunt animals in order to kill them. They can be killed accidentally by people in pursuit of quite different quarry.

Dolphins wander all over the oceans, especially where the water is warm, and they feed on fish. Fishing boats catching the same fish can trap dolphins in their nets. Dolphins are mammals and must surface to breathe air. If they are trapped inside nets, they are liable to drown and will certainly be injured by the battering they receive as the nets are hauled in.

Several species have been harmed in this way, but the one that received most publicity was the spinner dolphin (*Stenella longirostris*). It feeds on tuna, chasing the shoals in the open ocean and falling foul of the nets of fleets working the same shoals.

Popular pressure has succeeded in raising awareness of the problem in the fishing industry. Fishing methods have been modified, and dolphin deaths have been greatly reduced.

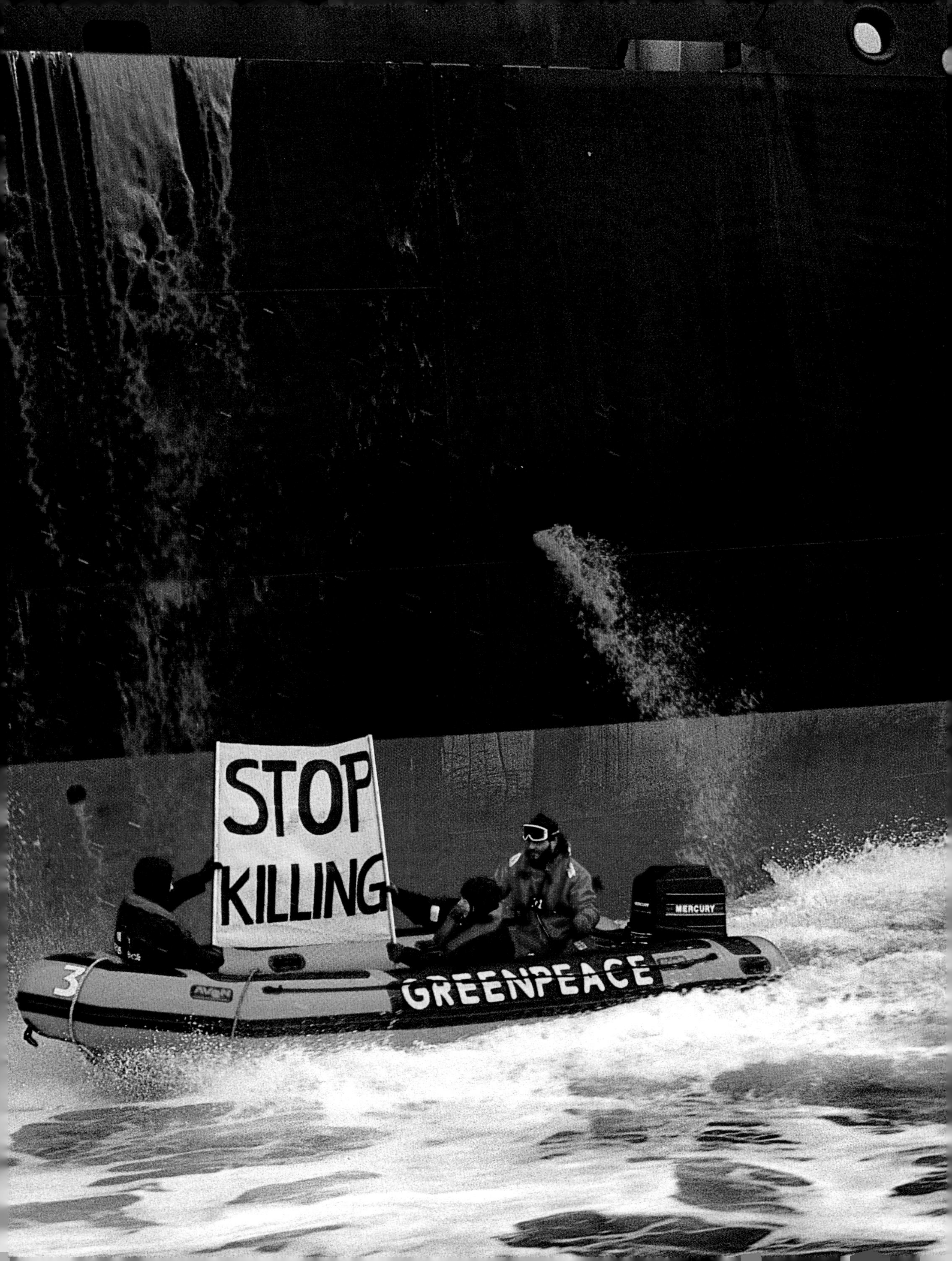

STOP
KILLING
GREENPEACE
MERCURY

Glossary

abyssal plain The deepest part of the ocean floor, below about 6,500 feet (2,000 m). This region accounts for approximately 75 percent of the total area of ocean floor.

adaptive radiation A rapid episode of evolution that occurs when new forms of an organism diversify from an ancestor that moved into an area offering a range of habitats its descendants could adapt to occupy.

alga A simple green plant that lacks true leaves, stem, and root. Many algae are single-celled; some are multicelled. Seaweeds are algae.

amphibian A vertebrate animal of the class Amphibia. The young develop in water, although the adults may live on land. Frogs, toads, newts, and salamanders are amphibians.

Antarctic Intermediate Water A mass of water that forms at about 50°S and spreads northward, sinking to about 3,000 feet (900 m). It can be detected in the North Atlantic as far north as about 25°N. The water is cold, with an average temperature of 36°F (2.2°C), and its salinity is low, averaging 33.8‰.

asthenosphere A region of the upper mantle in which the rock behaves like a solid that can be squeezed until it spreads and flows. The asthenosphere lies beneath the lithosphere, its upper margin about 60 miles (100 km) below the surface and its lower margin about 250 miles (400 km) below the surface.

atoll A circular island, or group of small islands approximately forming a circle, that is formed by a coral reef that has grown around the rim of the crater of a submarine volcano.

bacteria Microscopic organisms, most of which are single-celled, that are found in air, water, and soil everywhere. Different types vary in shape and way of life.

baleen Sheets of keratin (tough, fibrous material), with hairs fringing the lower edges, that hang from the roof of the mouth of a whale belonging to the suborder Mysticeti (baleen whales). The baleen resembles a comb and is used to filter from the water the plankton on which the whale feeds.

bathypelagic zone The region of the ocean at depths between 3,300 feet and 9,800 feet (1,000–3,000 m), where the water is uniformly cold, and no sunlight penetrates.

biome A large region throughout which living conditions for plants and animals are broadly similar, so the region can be classified according to its vegetation type.

carnivore An animal that feeds exclusively on other animals.

chlorophyll The green pigment, found in most plants, that absorbs light energy. This is then used to drive the reactions of photosynthesis.

consumer An organism that is unable to manufacture its own food from simple ingredients but must obtain it by eating (consuming) other organisms.

continental crust The rocks forming the crustal plates that bear continents and continental shelves. The rock is less dense than oceanic crust and therefore occupies a greater volume, which is why it projects above the ocean surface. Continental crust is mostly 19–25 miles (30–40 km) thick, but up to 43 miles (70 km) thick beneath mountain ranges.

continental drift The movement of continents across the surface of the Earth.

continental rise An accumulation of sediment at the foot of the continental slope. Its surface is smooth, and it slopes with a very gentle gradient, between 1:100 and 1:700.

continental shelf The surface of a continent that lies beneath the ocean, extending from the coast to the top of the continental slope, where the depth averages about 500 feet (150 m), on average about 43 miles (70 km) from the shore. The shelf slopes gently, with a gradient between 1:500 and 1:1,000.

continental slope The ocean floor extending 12–60 miles (20–100 km) from the bottom of the continental shelf to the top of the continental rise with an average gradient of 1:14.

convection Transfer of heat through a liquid or gas by the movement of the liquid or gas.

core The central part of the Earth, comprising a solid inner core with a diameter of about 1,550 miles (2,500 km) surrounded by a liquid outer core about 1,380 miles (2,220 km) thick.

crust The rock that makes up the outermost layer of the solid Earth, varying in thickness from about 3 miles (5 km) beneath some parts of the oceans to about 43 miles (70 km) beneath mountain ranges.

demersal Living close to the sea floor.

El Niño A weakening, cessation, or even reversal of the southeasterly trade winds in the Pacific Ocean immediately south of the equator. The change in the wind allows warm surface water to flood eastward and accumulate as a pool off the South American coast. Air crossing the warm water becomes warm and moist, bringing heavy rains to the ordinarily dry coastal strip. This phenomenon occurs every few years, and its effects are felt most strongly in December; hence the name, which refers to Jesus Christ and means, literally, "the (male) child." The opposite effect, called La Niña, intensifies the ordinary weather pattern. It is less common.

endemic Occurring naturally only in a particular region.

euphotic zone The upper region of the sea or ocean (or lake) in which sunlight penetrates sufficiently for photosynthesis to take place. It extends to a depth of about 100 feet (30 m) in coastal waters, but to 330–660 feet (100–200 m) in the clearer water of the open ocean.

eutrophic Highly enriched in nutrients.

gill **1** The organ with which an aquatic animal obtains oxygen from water. It consists of thin membranes with a large surface area over which water flows. Oxygen passes from the water through the walls of blood vessels in the gill membrane and into the blood. Most aquatic animals have two gills. **2** A bladelike structure in the fruiting body of a fungus (often the visible stage in the life of the fungus, such as a toadstool or mushroom) from which spores are released.

gyre A system of ocean currents that flows approximately in a circle in an ocean basin, moving counterclockwise in the Northern Hemisphere and clockwise in the Southern. There is a gyre in each of the oceans.

herbivore An animal that feeds exclusively on plants.

holdfast The structure by which an alga, such as a seaweed, is attached to a surface for anchorage. A holdfast may resemble a root or be disk-shaped and equipped with suckers.

hot spot A region in the mantle that is much hotter than its surroundings and produces volcanic activity in the overlying crust.

hurricane A tropical cyclone that occurs in the North Atlantic and Caribbean.

illicium The modified first fin ray of the dorsal fin of an angler fish that forms the "fishing pole," with a flap of skin at the tip as a lure.

invertebrate An animal that does not have a backbone.

lithosphere The outermost part of the solid Earth, comprising the rocks of the crust and the uppermost mantle. Its thickness ranges from 1 mile (1.6 km) or less at ocean ridges to 90 miles (145 km) beneath old ocean crust and 185 miles (298 km) beneath continents.

magma Molten rock produced by the melting of the lower part of the crust or upper part of the mantle.

mantle The region of the Earth lying between the crust and the core.

medusa A jellyfish; a soft-bodied animal shaped like an umbrella with tentacles hanging from the rim and a mouth at the center of the underside. It is the free-living stage in the life cycle of a cnidarian (Cnidaria is the phylum comprising sea anemones, jellyfish, and corals) and turns into a polyp that spends the rest of its life attached to a solid surface.

mesopelagic zone The region of the ocean that overlies the continental slope, from about 650 to 3,300 feet (200–1,000 m) below the surface.

North Atlantic Deep Water A mass of cold, saline water that forms near the edge of the sea ice, mainly in the Norwegian Sea, and sinks to the floor of the North Atlantic, where it flows south, eventually to Antarctic waters. Its temperature is 34–36.5°F (1–2.5°C).

omnivore An animal that eats food derived from both plants and animals.

pelagic Inhabiting the open seas and living well clear of the sea bed or, of sea birds, feeding at sea and coming ashore only to breed.

photosynthesis The series of chemical reactions by which green plants manufacture sugars, obtaining hydrogen from water and carbon from carbon dioxide, the energy driving the reactions being provided by light that is absorbed by chlorophyll.

plankton The small organisms that live near the surface of water and drift with movements of the water. They include single-celled plants (phytoplankton) and small animals (zooplankton), some of which are the larvae of fish and crustaceans.

plate tectonics The theory that the crust of the Earth is made up of a number of solid sections, called plates, that move in relation to each other. This explains continental drift and the spreading of the sea floors.

pod A small group of seals or whales.

polyp A soft-bodied, carnivorous animal, usually living attached to a surface, that is the sedentary form of a sea anemone or coral (the mobile form being a medusa). A polyp consists of a cylindrical trunk, attached to the surface at one end and with tentacles surrounding a mouth at the other end.

producer An organism, such as a green plant, that assembles large, complex substances from simple ingredients. These may then be eaten by consumers. On land the principal producers are green plants and in water they are phytoplankton (*see* plankton).

spermaceti Tissue that fills the enlarged snout of a sperm whale. It is well supplied with blood vessels and contains oils that solidify at about 90°F (32°C). Spermaceti may help the animal control its body temperature, may help it regulate its buoyancy, and may serve some function linked to echolocation.

subduction The sinking of one crustal plate beneath another made from rock that is less dense.

trade winds The prevailing and very dependable winds that blow on either side of the equator, from the northeast in the Northern Hemisphere and the southeast in the Southern Hemisphere.

tramp species A plant or animal species that has been carried around the world inadvertently by humans. Strangleweed or japweed (*Sargassum muticum*) has entered British coastal waters in this way, and water hyacinth (*Eichhornia crassipes*), native to South America, has been carried into tropical rivers on all continents. The house mouse (*Mus musculus*) is a tramp species that originated near the Russian–Turkish border.

tropics Those parts of the world that lie between latitudes 23°30'N and 23°30'S. These latitudes mark the boundaries of the region within which the Sun is directly overhead at noon on at least one day each year. The Tropic of Cancer is to the north of the equator and the Tropic of Capricorn to the south.

vertebrate An animal that has a backbone. Vertebrates also have a bony skull containing the brain and a skeleton made from bone or cartilage. Fish, amphibians, reptiles, birds, and mammals are vertebrates.

water table The uppermost margin of the ground water, below which the soil is saturated and above which it is not, although it is wet.

Further Reading

Basics of Environmental Science by Michael Allaby. Routledge.

Biology by Neil A. Campbell. The Benjamin/Cummings Publishing Co. Inc.

The Encyclopedia of Birds edited by Christopher M. Perrins and Alex L.A. Middleton. Facts on File.

The Encyclopedia of Insects edited by Christopher O'Toole. Facts on File.

The Encyclopedia of Mammals edited by David Macdonald. Facts on File.

The Encyclopedia of Reptiles and Amphibians edited by Tim Halliday and Kraig Adler. Facts on File.

Flowering Plants of the World edited by V.H. Heywood. Oxford University Press, New York.

Green Planet edited by David M. Moore. Cambridge University Press.

The Hunters by Philip Whitfield. Simon and Schuster.

Hutchinson Encyclopedia of the Earth edited by Peter J. Smith. Hutchinson.

The Lie of the Land edited by K.J. Gregory. Oxford University Press, New York.

Longman Illustrated Animal Encyclopedia edited by Philip Whitfield. Guild Publishing.

The Oxford Encyclopedia of Trees of the World edited by Bayard Hora. Oxford University Press, New York.

Planet Earth: Cosmology, Geology, and the Evolution of Life and Environment by Cesare Emiliani. Cambridge University Press.

Snakes of the World by Chris Mattison. Blandford Press Ltd.

The Science of Ecology by Richard Brewer. Saunders College Publishing, Harcourt Brace College Publishers.

Ecosystems: Oceans by Trevor Day. Facts on File.

The Encyclopedia of Aquatic Life edited by Keith Banister and Andrew Campbell. Facts on File.

Marine Biology by James W. Nybakken. HarperCollins College Publishers.

Web sites:

Ocean 1998 is a program of information and environmental protection, with a site at: http://www.ocean98.org/ocean98.html

Ocean Planet is a traveling exhibition from the Smithsonian Institution, Washington. It has its own site, with descriptions of the exhibits, at: http://seawifs.gsfc.nasa.gov/ocean_planet.html

The Independent World Commission on the Oceans, led by the former prime minister of Portugal, is at: http://www.world-oceans.org/

Photographic Acknowledgments

7 ESA/Photo Library International/Science Photo Library; **9** Peter Ryan/Scripps/Science Photo Library; **11** NASA/Science Photo Library; **14** Peter Scoones/Planet Earth Pictures; **23** V. Taylor/Ardea London; **35** Jacana; **41** NASA/Science Photo Library; **44** S. Osolinski/Oxford Scientific Films; **52** Doug Perrino/Planet Earth Pictures; **55** Culley/Greenpeace Communications; **Cover pictures:** *top:* Fritz Prenzel/Bruce Coleman Limited; *bottom*: David Hughes/Bruce Coleman Limited; *globe motif:* Terra Forma™ Copyright© 1995–1997 Andromeda Interactive Ltd.

Set Index

Page numbers in *italics* refer to illustrations; volume numbers are in **bold**.

F

G

U

V

W

X-Y

Z